ᴳ

Professional and Reference Books, an imprint of TAB BOOKS.
a division of McGraw-Hill, Inc.
ᵢional and Reference Books logo, consisting of the letters "TPR"
'," is a registered trademark of TAB BOOKS.

gress Cataloging-in-Publication Data

V.
es on HVAC controls / by Roger W. Haines.

dex.
6-7625-2
–Control—Miscellanea.   2. Air conditioning—Control—
.   I. Title.
5   1990
              90-44416
              CIP

ers software for sale. For information and a catalog, please contact
epartment, Blue Ridge Summit, PA 17294-0850.

ᵈing the content of this book should be addressed to:

Branch

mmit, PA 17294-0850

ᵈ Editorial Director: Larry Hager
rine G. Brown
ᵢyn J. Boone

Roger Hai
on HVAC C

Roger W. Hain

FIRST EDITIO
FIRST PRINTI

© 1991 by T
TAB BOOKS
The TAB Prof
within a large

Printed in the
responsibility
nor for the pr

Library of C

Haines, Roge
    Roger H
    p.
    Includes
    ISBN 0-8
    1. Heati
    Miscella
TH7466.5
697—dc2

TAB BOOKS
TAB Softwar

Questions re

Reader Inq
TAB BOOK
Blue Ridge

TAB Professional and Refe

Division of TAB BOOKS

Blue Ridge Summit, PA

Vice Presiden
Production: K
Book Design

Contents

Part 2

Theory

Part 3

Systems and subsystems

Part 4

Control devices

Part 5

Computer-based control systems

Acknowledgments

As always, I owe a great debt to many people. First and foremost I want to thank Bob Korte (editor) and Ted Pannkoke (engineering editor) of *Heating/ Piping/Air Conditioning* magazine for their courtesy, patience, and encouragement over the years, and for giving me permission to republish the material in book form. Larry Hager has been a friend as well as an editor and encouraged me to put this book together. The letters and phone calls I got from readers of the columns were always appreciated even, or especially, when they took me to task for errors. And, as she has done for nearly 50 years, my wife gave me love and support.

Introduction

From 1980 to 1987, I wrote a series of columns for *Heating/Piping/Air Conditioning* magazine under the title of "Roger Haines on Controls." At the time these articles received a favorable response and, from time to time, I considered the possibility of publishing them in book form.

Recently, Larry Hager, my friend and editor, asked me if I could write another book. After some consideration, I remembered the columns, and Larry agreed to publish the collection. So here they are.

I was somewhat concerned about problems with obsolete technology and expected to do considerable editing. Although I have done some editing, it was a pleasant surprise to find that most of what I wrote then is still valid. I call this the result of Haines' law of control design: "Technology changes; fundamentals do not change." I have attempted to cover some of the technological changes with comments at the end of some sections. I have omitted a few articles that were not salvageable. To be honest, I wish I had not written some of them.

When written, the columns followed no specific order to theme but simply reflected whatever was on my mind that month. For the book I have attempted to group them under five general topics: philosophy, theory, systems and subsystems, control devices, and computer-based control systems. Many of the items cannot be clearly classified, so I simply was arbitrary. But you will find philosophy and theory almost anywhere you look. It is my opinion that no one can be a competent control designer without a consistent philosophy.

I made no attempt in this book to present an orderly exposition of how to design control systems. But you will find, I hope, a great many useful ideas and suggestions. That was the idea in publishing the columns, now continued in this collection.

Part 1

Philosophy

It has been said that engineering is the antithesis of art. With all its formulae and rules to be observed, engineering is often called a *discipline*. But art, too, requires discipline. Be assured, by an amateur musician with experience in both vocal and instrumental music, that music — one of the arts — requires a great deal of discipline. The same is true for painting, sculpture, literature, and all the rest, though some of the modern artists would have you believe otherwise. Any of these arts require you to start with a basic set of values or criteria that you use in performing and judging our work. This is simply the definition of *philosophy* — a set of values by which you judge your actions.

It is essential that you approach all engineering problems with a philosophy that transcends the rules and formulae and that allows you to be flexible and creative, while still staying within the physical laws that govern engineering design. You need to understand how those laws were developed, what they imply in a given situation, and how they can be helpful rather than irksome.

This section discusses philosophical, rather than technical questions, although there is often some overlap. Each of you should develop your own philosophy, remembering that one of the fundamental philosophical values is that basic values can change with time and experience. Please stay flexible and open to new ideas, but evaluate them carefully before you adopt them.

Solving control problems
through system upgrading*

Consulting engineers spend a great deal of time investigating existing HVAC (heating, ventilating, and air conditioning) systems and their controls. Typically, the client wants the system to perform better, in terms of comfort or process requirements, and to use less energy. Also, it is usually possible to accomplish both.

The expression, "You've seen one, you've seen 'em all," could very easily be applied to the HVAC systems in the industrial and institutional buildings we study. In general, HVAC systems fall into three classes:

1. Systems that were designed in the days of cheap energy: for example, dual-duct, multizone, and terminal reheat systems.
2. Control systems that were originally well designed but have been "weakened" by operating personnel until nothing works as intended.
3. Systems that have the potential for good, energy-saving control but have poorly designed controls, which make energy conservation difficult or impossible.

The symptoms of category 2 problems appear in almost all cases. Typically, the operating person understands very little of system theory but knows from experience how to adjust certain controls to satisfy complaints. How the adjustment affects the rest of the system or energy consumption is not nearly so important as getting a department manager stop complaining. After a few years of this practice, any resemblance between current and theoretical performance is purely illusory.

Category 3 problems are more subtle. Some control systems appear to be well designed—if one could just figure out how they work. Some degree of complexity might be necessary for a sophisticated HVAC system, but the rule of simplicity still applies. Most complex systems can be greatly simplified and still respond to the original criteria.

A category 1 problem is a system, rather than a control, problem. The solutions include changes in both the HVAC system and the controls.

Now, if problems are typical, shouldn't there be some quick, easy, typical solutions? Your answer is, of course, "If the solutions were easy they wouldn't need me." How, then, do you proceed?

Step 1 is to test the existing system to find out what it is actually doing. Do not rely on the system instrumentation. Use a set of calibrated test gauges and thermometers. Check for leaking control valves, a frequent cause of energy waste. Sometimes recalibration and replacement of a few defective devices will work wonders.

---

*May 1980.

Step 2 is obvious, yet often neglected. If you were starting fresh, how would you do it? What are the criteria? If the system is for comfort only, then follow energy-saving guidelines — that is, 78 degrees F in summer, 68 degrees F in winter. If the system serves a process, such as electronic manufacturing or hospital surgery, you need close control at a specific temperature and humidity. In either case, the control methods can make a great difference in energy consumption. Therefore, given the specific criteria, how would you design the control system to meet the criteria with minimum energy use? Perhaps a change in the HVAC system is needed.

Step 3 is to compare your ideal system with the existing system. Sometimes the differences are minor. If major differences exist, indicating an expensive retrofit, an economic analysis might be required to compare retrofit costs with potential energy savings or other benefits. If the existing and ideal are essentially identical, then it is only necessary to ensure that the system works as designed — recalibrate, adjust, and test.

Someone might complain that nothing is said about energy management systems. Certainly energy management has its place, though not all energy management systems really manage energy. But supervising an inefficient HVAC system will not improve it nearly so much as proper redesign of the system. A supervisory system is merely the frosting on the cake — something you do after you have done all the other good things. It is not a substitute for good HVAC design and maintenance, but it can be used to minimize degradation in HVAC system performance.

The real key to upgrading an HVAC system and controls is a proper understanding of how the system is supposed to work. First draw a system schematic, showing temperatures, pressures, flow rates, and other pertinent data (FIG. 1-1). Then plot the cycle on a psychometric chart using winter and summer design conditions and some intermediate conditions as well (FIG. 1-2). If there is difficulty with this step, it might be the fault of the system design. The psychrometric chart analysis will also show areas where energy can be conserved and should suggest system changes needed.

Careful study of these two pictures usually makes the control strategy obvious. All that is required then is a knowledge of what control strategies work in a given situation.

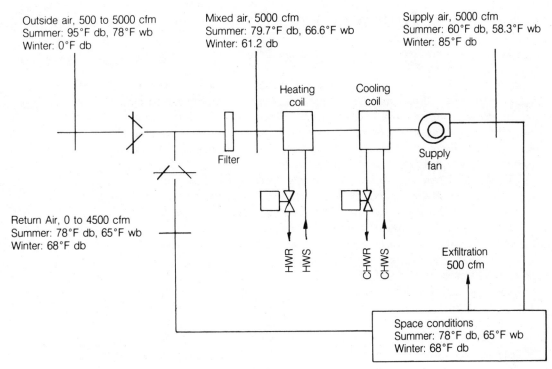

Outside air, 500 to 5000 cfm
Summer: 95°F db, 78°F wb
Winter: 0°F db

Mixed air, 5000 cfm
Summer: 79.7°F db, 66.6°F wb
Winter: 61.2 db

Supply air, 5000 cfm
Summer: 60°F db, 58.3°F wb
Winter: 85°F db

Heating
coil

Cooling
coil

Filter

Supply
fan

Return Air, 0 to 4500 cfm
Summer: 78°F db, 65°F wb
Winter: 68°F db

HWR   HWS

CHWR   CHWS

Exfiltration
500 cfm

Space conditions
Summer: 78°F db, 65°F wb
Winter: 68°F db

Fig. 1-1. System flow diagram.

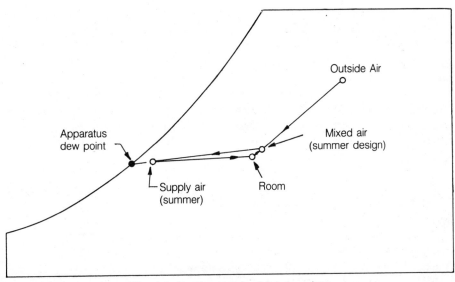

Outside Air

Apparatus
dew point

Mixed air
(summer design)

Supply air
(summer)

Room

Fig. 1-2. Psychrometric chart for system.

Reminiscence*

While cleaning out my files, I came across a number of memory-triggering items from the past. I'd like to reminisce a bit.

One of the items I found was an article I wrote for the June 1970 issue of *Heating/Piping/Air Conditioning.* "Where Are We Headed in Computerized Control" grew out of my work in facilities engineering at Collins Radio Company and discussed the advent of computer supervision and control of environmental systems. It discussed services the computer would provide and advised engineers to study and get in on the ground floor.

The article turned out to be a reasonably accurate forecast. Actually, given an inside look at the trends in the electronic industry, it was not that hard to be a prophet. We could see the minicomputer coming because Collins actually had one at the time — developed for use with airborne navigational systems. But we did not foresee the microcomputer because the silicon chip was still experimental; we were trying to make conventional circuit boards smaller. The transistor was still a big item.

Looking back, it is absolutely amazing to see what happened in electronics in the decade of the 1970s — and to see what still is happening. Development seems to increase at an exponential rate. Where does it all end? That is for someone else to say. I am out of the predicting business.

Looking back, for me, means looking at over 28 years of experience as a consulting engineer and enjoying every minute of it. Well, almost. I am fortunate to have found an occupation so interesting, rewarding and enjoyable. This is why I write. A long time ago an older engineer said to me, "We have an obligation to give back something to the profession that has given us so much."

One of the best parts of my experience has been involvement in ASHRAE (American Society of Heating, Refrigeration, and Air Conditioning Engineers, Inc.), primarily on technical committees. This is a superb way to learn, contribute and make friends. I recommend it to everyone.

Throughout my experience, I have learned the truth of that old cliche, "You're never too old to learn." The real problem with getting older is that there is so much to "unlearn." The years have demonstrated the veracity of that observation many times. Several of my cherished absolutes have been shown not to be so absolute. That keeps life interesting, too.

*   *   *

The most interesting thing about the above article is that even eight years later, the basic ideas I expressed in 1970 were still valid. The technology, and especially the software, have become still more sophisticated but the fundamentals have not changed. All of this tends to verify Haines' first law of control design, "Technology changes; fundamentals do not change."

---

*December 1981.

MCS debate*

A reader writes

"I am writing to help settle an argument regarding MCS (monitoring and control systems). The following are some points that need clarifying:

1. Duty cycling does not save energy. Temperature drift is such that energy saved is lost to overcome the increased load.
2. No savings (fan power consumption) can be achieved by the duty cycling of a VAV (variable air volume) system. This is based on the same argument as item 1.
3. Duty cycling in a hospital, for example, is a code violation even in noncritical areas.
4. No energy input savings can be achieved via the duty cycling of chillers, boilers, or fans.
5. Duty cycling increases wear and tear on motors and belts, and it increases energy consumption because of startup.
6. A properly installed, programmed, and applied MCS will not save 25 percent of a hospital energy bill.

"I would appreciate your comments on these items. I love your articles; keep up the good work."

Roger Haines replies

Thank you for your letter and compliments on my column. Your questions on MCS have been raised by a number of people and are still being debated. For most of the questions there are no definite data, but some consensus is beginning to arise. Some of the answers can be calculated theoretically, and others cannot. There are many things here that need some research before you can definitely prove or disprove them.

However, to answer your questions:

1. Duty cycling does save energy. If you turn a fan off for, say, 10 minutes out of each hour, there must be a saving in fan energy. The brief surge at restart does not negate the savings. Thermal energy savings are minimal, at best, because set point conditions must be restored (but energy required to condition outside air is saved). The real question is: "Is this the best way to save energy?" The answer is, "No." If the HVAC has enough extra capacity to restore conditions after a shutdown, why not slow down the fan and run it continuously? That will

---

*July 1983.

save more energy than duty cycling and will provide a better environment. Of course, this logic ultimately leads you to VAV.

2. VAV systems should not be duty cycled because no fan energy would be saved, as analysis will show. See the answer to item 1. In fact, more fan energy might be used! The reasoning behind that statement is that fan horsepower varies as the cube of flow rate.

3. Duty cycling might be a code violation if ventilation rate code requirements are not met. This problem is encountered in hospitals. Local codes will apply, so no specific statements can be made. Your general thesis is sound.

4. See the answer to item 1. Thermal energy can be saved by cycling only at the expense of environmental control. For boilers particularly, cycling decreases overall efficiency and can increase energy consumption. Fan energy can be saved by duty cycling.

5. Most building operators and engineers agree that duty cycling increases maintenance and shortens equipment life. It especially affects belts, bearings, motors, and motor starters.

6. A properly installed, programmed, and utilized MCS will save some part of the building energy bill. Most of the 25 to 35 percent claims are based on the MCS installation plus a general upgrading of the HVAC systems, controls and operating procedures. What part of this is solely attributable to the MCS is in question.

Some fairly reliable data is available from a few sources that indicate that a 10 percent saving due to MCS is probably in the right order of magnitude. For example, a large manufacturer installed 111 MCS at 215 plants and kept records that indicated that the energy savings attributable to the MCS alone ranged from 7 to 10 percent. An additional factor, which you did not mention, is the need to upgrade the skills and motivation of operating and maintenance personnel when an MCS is installed. Failure to address this can lead to total failure of the MCS.

We are now in the process of writing a manual on MCS for the guidance of building owners and operators and design engineers which will address these and many other questions. Thank you for writing.

*   *   *

The manual referenced in this section is: "Guidelines for the Design and Purchase of Energy Management and Control Systems for New and Retrofit Applications," published by the American Consulting Engineers Council in March 1984. Although the technology described in the manual is somewhat outdated, the principles of evaluating and selecting a system are still very valid. In response to a letter from another reader, I noted that the conclusions in the manual included:

1. An MCS will not cure a sick control system. All local loop controls and HVAC systems must be properly maintained and upgraded before an MCS can be of value.
2. If the MCS is to be satisfactory, it is essential that the owner and the managers make a commitment to hire and train competent operators and maintenance personnel and to create an environment in which these people can function efficiently.
3. The design and construction of an MCS requires very careful analysis to determine all necessary functions and eliminate those that are not needed.
4. If the existing systems are brought up to maximum efficiency, the need for an MCS is not so acute and might not be economically justified. Each case needs careful study.

Closed-loop control of energy*

Among EMCS (energy management and control system) topics are three important points:

1. An EMCS is not a magic solution that will overcome deficiencies in the HVAC systems and controls.
2. A properly designed and operated EMCS will save energy, though not in the amounts claimed by some proponents.
3. Even when properly designed and operated according to current state-of-the-art procedures, the EMCS might not conserve enough energy to justify its expense.

I would like to discuss a concept that is only hinted at in current technology but that easily could be the best justification yet for using EMCS: the concept of the EMCS as a closed-loop system with energy consumption as the controlled variable.

Closed-loop control

For those who are not clear on the distinction between open- and closed-loop control, a brief review is in order.

In the classic closed loop control system as shown in FIG. 1-3, the principal elements are:

1. The *controlled variable*, which in this case, is the supply air temperature.
2. The *sensor*.

---

*December 1983.

3. The *controller*, which compares the sensed value with a *setpoint* and uses the difference between the two (called the *error*) to generate an output signal.
4. The *controlled device*, which in this case is a valve controlling the flow of hot water or steam to a heating coil.
5. The *process plant*, which in this case includes the heating coil and the air stream.

As the valve is repositioned by the controller output signal, the temperature of the air stream will change. This change will be sensed and communicated to the controller, a new output signal will be generated, the valve will be repositioned, and the whole process will be repeated. Notice that the controlled variable is directly affected by the change in the controller output. The process of sensing this change and using it is known as *feedback* and is an essential property of a closed loop system.

If the sensed variable is not the controlled variable and is not directly affected by the controller output, the system is said to be an *open loop* control. This is illustrated in FIG. 1-4, which is the same as FIG. 1-3 but with an outside air temperature sensor used to reset the setpoint of the controller. Because the outside air temperature is not affected by the controller action, this portion of the control system is open loop.

Application to EMCS

Now, how does closed-loop control make an EMCS more effective? The present software approach is to work with each of the individual systems within a complex. The system makes adjustments (reset, etc.) to meet some arbitrary standard of performance, which might or might not minimize the energy consumption of that system. In terms of energy, this is open-loop control because energy consumption is not being measured.

What, then, would be necessary for the EMCS to become a closed-loop system in terms of energy consumption?

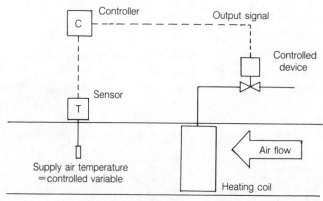

Fig. 1-3. Closed-loop control system.

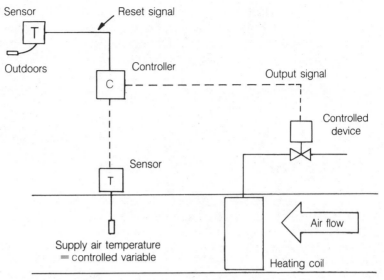

Fig. 1-4. Closed-loop control system with reset.

There are, obviously, a great many variables involved. These include the operating status of the air-handling systems, chiller plant condition (including efficiencies, pump operation and cooling tower operation), heating plant conditions, weather, building occupancy, time of day, and building environmental conditions. The idea would be to evaluate all these data and determine the operating parameters for all parts of the system which would lead to an overall minimum energy consumption.

When you look at all the possible complexities, it is easy to understand that the problem has been approached only in limited ways. There are, for example, chiller plant optimization programs that attempt to maximize the overall efficiency by measuring load as a function of chilled water flow, supply temperatures, and return temperatures. These programs adjust output to match the measured load conditions.

Some programs even adjust pumping speeds and capacities to minimize pump horsepower. A few also adjust condensing water temperatures. Even these programs, however, use arbitrary performance standards and do not continuously measure overall chiller plant energy use.

The ideal program would monitor all of the variables and measure energy consumption. Variables would be classified in the order of their effect on overall energy consumption. Starting with the greatest-effect variable, one variable at a time would be adjusted until energy consumption was minimized, then the next variable would be adjusted, and so on. (Or a complex algorithm might be written.) Typically, if all space temperatures and humidities were satisfied, chilled water temperatures could be adjusted upward, with all that follows in the central plant. However, that adjustment would be limited by the need for an acceptable environment in all spaces. So adjustments to air flow rates, pumping capacity, etc., might become necessary.

It is a very complex situation. Perhaps this is why so little has been done. The various purveyors of EMCS software have surely looked at the problem and the costs and have surely concluded that the time is not yet ripe.

Someday the EMCS must be allowed to become what its name implies: a system for really monitoring and controlling overall energy consumption in the most efficient manner possible. Then those 25 to 30 percent savings that are so blithely claimed might become real.

Education in controls needed*

Instead of the usual technical discussion, the philosophical comments that follow relate not only to the topic of *controls* but even more to the attitude toward HVAC work.

The most disturbing thing is the phone calls, mostly from owners. The typical call goes something like this:

"We have just bid (or are installing) an energy management system. The specifications were written around the equipment of Vendor A, but Vendor B was the low bidder. Now we have submittals (or the job is being installed), and our design engineer doesn't really know whether Vendor B meets the specifications or not. Who can we get to help us?"

This problem relates to everyone in the HVAC industry. The owner is not a technical person, although an institutional owner will usually have some reasonably competent people on his staff. But the owner expects the results promised by the sales person and the designer.

The person who has to achieve those results is the operator. If lucky the operator might get a few hours of quick explanation from the sales person. The operator might never see the designer. After all, for such a low fee, who can afford to go back and support the operator? So to get back to the basic rule of control design: "No matter what you design, the operator will reduce it to his or her level of understanding." This rule saved us when energy was cheap and systems were simple, with plenty of knobs and dials to "tweak." An experienced operator could almost always manage to keep it comfortable. With low-cost energy, who cared about a few extra Btus (British thermal units)? Now the owner has become more cost conscious and sophisticated. At the same time control systems are becoming more complex as we attempt to save energy. With local loop DDC (direct digital control) we use the computer to replace the conventional controllers and the knobs and dials disappear. We can only tweak numbers in software!

What all this means is that although there is a considerable knowledge gap about the old pneumatic and electrical controls, a whole new, rapidly changing, technology is here. If you do not understand basic control theory, you are going to be lost.

---

*May 1984.

Everyone needs to learn more — a lot more — and quickly. Here are a few suggestions:

1. Read and study the available reference books in the field, including *Control Systems for HVAC*. The ASHRAE Handbook has good information on controls.
2. Read the technical articles in *Heating/Piping/Air Conditioning* and the ASHRAE Journal. If you need more explanation write to the authors. They are always willing to help.
3. Go to ASHRAE meetings — local, regional, and national. Attend the technical sessions. Ask questions. No question is stupid if you do not know the answer.
4. Go to the ASHRAE Professional Development Seminars (PDS). PDS-2 covers local-loop controls. PDS-4 deals with computer-based supervisory control systems and DDC. Contact ASHRAE headquarters for information.
5. If you have a particular problem of a general nature, write to the author of this book.
6. Above all, learn fundamentals so that the owner cannot call to complain that you cannot evaluate a substitute submittal! The motto for all design professionals, contractors and salesmen should be: "Support your local owner."

*   *   *

In recent years, I have made a great deal of money responding to the owner's problems similar to those described above. While I don't mind the extra income, I greatly dislike the shadow these things cast on the technical competence of the HVAC consulting profession. I'd much rather hear positive things and make less money. Then we'll all benefit. You could say, you owe it to your profession to be as well educated as possible!

Operating HVAC systems*

If you have been doing your homework and studying everything available on controls, you should be well on your way to becoming a competent control system designer. So you apply your expertise to design and specifications, and you even lean on the contractor to get the system properly installed and operating. Now everything is working as designed and there should be no more problems. Right?

Wrong!

One of the "natural laws" pertaining to HVAC control systems is this: "The operator will reduce the system to his or her level of understanding."

---

*July 1984.

This is not to criticize the operator. All too often the operator is handed the system with a few brief words from the contractor or designer and left without further help, with no real concept of how the system should work or what it can (and cannot) do.

If the system is to be operated as designed, the operator must have adequate documentation about the system and accurate information feedback on actual system performance. Documentation includes schematic diagrams, operating sequences, instructions, and maintenance manuals.

Schematic diagrams must reflect all of the as-built changes accurately. They should be provided by the contractor, but the designer must make a final check. Typically, they are framed under glass and posted in the machine room. Prints must be permanent—no blueprints or prints that might fade. Even some photographs are subject to fading. Identification symbols or colors used on wire and tubing should be shown on the diagrams.

An operating sequence is a step-by-step description of how the system is supposed to perform. Preferably, it should include some discussion of system philosophy and intent. Instructions can be in simple cookbook form or more generalized, whichever better serves the purpose of informing the operator. Operating sequences, too, should be posted in the machine room at the control panel.

Maintenance manuals include servicing instructions (what to do and when to do it) and parts lists. They should also include calibration procedures with expected accuracies. The accuracy and credibility of calibration depends largely on the quality of the instruments used. A pocket thermometer with a 1-inch dial and a pressure gauge with a 1½ inch dial should not be considered adequate for calibration.

Now with all this documentation, the operator's understanding should approach that of the designer's. But the operator still cannot operate the system to the desired level without an information feedback system that monitors the operation.

The preferred procedure is a control cabinet that has all of the system controllers and relays in it. The face of the cabinet should have indicators showing temperatures, humidities, pressures, and flow rates. Typically with an air system, the indicators would show supply, return, outside, and mixed air temperatures; duct pressure (if applicable); filter pressure drop; supply (and return) fan status; minimum outside air setting; and any other pertinent data. Good quality and credibility of these devices are essential if they are to be relied upon and used. All that was said about maintenance and calibration applies here, too. In selecting system indicators, ask yourself what the operator needs to know to operate the system most effectively. Then provide that information.

Now that you have done all this, is it enough? Not quite. Now, sit down with the operator to make sure he or she understands all that has been provided. Tell the operator to call if problems arise. Then leave system operation to the operator, assured that you have done your best.

*   *   *

The typical design professional who reads this section poses two questions:

1. How do I determine what devices are good and credible?
2. How can I spend all that time and effort when I get such a low fee?

The answer to question 1 is to look at experience—your own and that of others—to see what does and does not work. This means that you have to go back to old jobs and talk to the operators.

The answer to question 2 is education. You need to make owners and architects aware of the penalty implied in underpaying the mechanical and electrical designer.

There is another problem. Regardless of the fee, when the HVAC system does not work properly, the designer gets to spend some time trying to fix it. That time might well have been spent avoiding the problems and thereby improving the designer's credibility.

Monitoring and control without computers*

Among the many advantages claimed for a computer-based MCS (monitoring and control system) is that of obtaining, displaying, and recording accurate operating data for HVAC systems. This has been an effective argument for the use of computers because very few existing local-loop control systems have useful monitoring devices. Even for those few that have control panels with gauges and indicators, the credibility of the information is low because of poor maintenance and lack of regular calibration.

It does not need to be this way. It is possible to provide reliable and accurate monitoring without computers. As usual, you need to get back to basic principles.

What is the purpose of monitoring? Good information about HVAC system performance will indicate that the system is operating properly or, if not, what the anomalies are, so that a knowledgeable operator can correct them. If corrections are made promptly, the building occupants might not be aware that a problem existed. This makes everybody happy, especially the operator.

---

*October 1984.

What is needed to obtain good monitoring? There is no simple cookbook answer to that question since every system is different. But there are some principles that can be applied.

First, you must ask what information is needed to ensure that the system is operating properly. Space temperature is certainly useful but, in by itself provides no warning of system anomalies or imminent failure. Supply air temperature, combined with space temperature, should give you some idea of the load and how well it is being met. In a multizone or dual-duct system, this would mean hot and cold plenum temperatures as well. In a variable-volume system, you would like to know that the control-point static pressure is being maintained and which fan speed or inlet vane damper position maintains it. If there is an economy cycle, you need to know return air, outside air, and mixed air temperatures. Status of fan motors and alarm conditions is also needed. All this is for a typical, simple HVAC system. If there are special requirements, such as humidity or space pressurization, additional monitoring is needed.

The other essential factor in monitoring is credibility. If the operator does not believe the data presented to him, the monitoring system will be ignored. Two things are necessary for establishing and maintaining credibility: (1) accurate, high-quality sensors and indicators and (2) a program of regular maintenance and calibration.

Temperature sensors should preferably be wound-wire platinum resistance temperature detectors or thin-film platinum. The thin-film platinum needs to be checked at least once a year. Thermisters are good but need more frequent calibration—two or three times a year. Bulb and capillary or rod-and-tube sensors are less accurate because of mechanical hysteresis, and they tend to have low credibility.

Pressure sensors of the *piezoelectric* (strain gage) type are recommended for low pressures—0 to 4 inches wc (water column) gauge. If slack diaphragm sensors are used, they should be industrial quality with 9-inch or larger diaphragms and must be calibrated at least two or three times a year.

Humidity sensors for general use should be thin- or thick-film absorbent, capacitance, or resistance types. These usually have a guaranteed accuracy of plus or minus three percent rh (relative humidity), with a drift of about one percent per year. Yearly recalibration is required. If even higher accuracies are required, use a chilled-mirror dewpoint sensor. This device has low maintenance requirements (occasional cleaning of the mirror), and it can be used for calibration of other humidity instruments.

If monitoring of analog points is electronic, a digital display meter (or meters) can be used. A multiposition selector switch allows one meter to be used for several points.

Two-position status, including alarms, can be shown by means of pilot lights. A push-to-test switch allows the operator to test these at any time.

To obtain a record over time, use a recording device. Circular or strip chart recorders are available. Circular chart recorders can be 24 hour or seven-day type with up to three or four variables recorded simultaneously.

Strip recorders can track several variables simultaneously for fairly long periods. A wide variety of such devices is available.

As already noted, regular maintenance and recalibration are required to maintain credibility. Proper recalibration requires the use of laboratory-quality instruments with accuracies equal to or better than those of the device being calibrated. This requires that the calibrator understand the principles of operation of the systems and devices being checked. So here you are, full circle, back to education and training.

Summing up, it is possible to provide good monitoring without using a computer. It has been done for years. If your system is large and you need much data, a computer might be, by comparison, less expensive. There is no hard-and-fast rule here. Just remember, there are options.

Organizing controls for a large complex*

A reader writes

"I read 'Roger Haines on Controls' in HPAC each month and have the book *Control Systems for Heating, Ventilating and Air Conditioning*, which my shop uses as its training manual. I would like your advice on my situation. I am foreman of the HVAC controls shop at _____ (a large air base). I have three civilian and seven young military personnel to maintain the HVAC controls on this very large installation. The controls are electric, electronic, and pneumatic for both comfort and environmentally controlled areas. Due to command policy, we have heating available three months each year, cooling available three months each year, and nothing but outside air available for six months each year.

"We have mandatory temperatures of 70 degrees F in winter and 78 degrees F in summer. Our problem is trying to maintain a large number of complicated systems with so few personnel. We have talked to the design engineers about giving us systems that would allow us to control to the required temperatures, not be complicated with extra components, be easily maintained, and maximize the utilization of outside air. Because we never have heating and cooling available at the same time in comfort-controlled areas, we have experimented with using a summer-winter switch to separate the heating and cooling and an outside air stat to lock out the mechanical-heating until the outside air falls to 72 degrees F and lock out the mechanical cooling until the outside air rises to 76 degrees F.

"We have electric, electronic and pneumatic controls on air handling with direct expansion cooling and chilled water from our central plant. We don't feel that a system has to be cluttered with a large number of components to be

*January 1985.

effective. Any suggestions, information or advice you can offer will be greatly appreciated and used."

Roger Haines replies

As you are probably aware, your situation is typical of most military bases and of many institutional applications. So, in answering your letter, I want to address all those other maintenance people, too.

To enlarge somewhat on your system description: I would expect that you are dealing with about 100 buildings ranging in size from guard shacks to large hangars, with usage including housing, post exchange, administration, aircraft maintenance, shops, fire department, hospital, schools, recreation, and many other things. In other words, a small city. These buildings have been constructed over a period of 40 to 50 years with a broad range of design criteria, many different designers, and degrees of sophistication ranging from the guard shack to a modern flight simulator.

Your first step in problem solving is education, starting with your supervisor. It has always amazed me that institutional managers seem totally unaware of the fact that the systems for controlling the environment in their buildings represent as much as 20 to 30 percent of the capital cost, affect the productivity of all workers, and consume as much as two thirds of the total energy used by the facility. Extra money for maintenance and operation, if wisely used as described, can return large dividends. With or without any additional funds, I would suggest a four-step program.

1. Education. The education is for you and all of your mechanics. Make sure your people read the appropriate books and trade journal articles. Read anything else you can find that applies. As you go through steps 2, 3, and 4, everyone in your organization should be involved — listening, commenting, objecting, and most of all, learning. Maintenance people need to know what a device looks like and how to repair it, but they also need to know how and why it functions in the overall scheme. They need to understand why one scheme is used rather than another. Get the manufacturer's service literature for every device you have (if you have not done so already).
2. Develop as-built (as-existing) control schematics and sequences of operation. This will take time, but it is worth thousands of dollars when you are ready to revise and automate a system. The schematics are line drawings showing all control devices, how they relate to the HVAC system, and how they are connected to one another (wires, tubes, etc.). You will want device names, manufacturers, and model numbers (if you can still find them!). Wiring should include conduit indication and voltage and current. While you are tracking this down, you have an excellent opportunity to label everything. Do it!

   The drawings need to be neat, clear, explicit, and complete. Fancy drawings are not necessary. Cross-section paper 11 by 17 or 17 by 22 inches is very useful.

The sequence is simply a brief written description of how the system works.

Getting the information is the hard part. Maybe it looks impossible with your schedule. Perhaps you can get the money to hire an independent control contractor to do it for you. It is a large task. If you presently have the data for 10 percent of your systems, you are better off than most. It is an essential step in any long-run simplification or standardization program. Incidentally, once you have these data, keep everything up to date as changes are made. You know about changes, right?

3. Simplify and standardize. This depends on the data you have gathered in step 2, but it does not have to wait for data on the whole base. Patterns will begin to emerge fairly early on, so that typical situations can be described and standardization begun. Now you know how the various manufacturers carry out a particular function. Modern commercial pneumatic controls have very small air passages. The resulting low volumes often make it necessary to add amplifiers on control outputs to valves and dampers. Industrial pneumatic controls typically have high-volume outputs and do not need amplifiers. The result is a simpler system.

4. Revise HVAC systems. If there are a dozen versions of a single zone air handler, then a dozen control systems are required. Work with the HVAC equipment group to revise systems to allow standardization. This is essential if outside air cycles are to be used. This follows from the conclusions reached in step 3 and depends on the concurrence and cooperation of the HVAC equipment group.

You might want to consider the advantages of base-wide pneumatic or electric controls to improve simplification. This would certainly not be an overnight transition but could be a long-range program. My own preference is for electronic sensing and control with pneumatic operators for valves and dampers. In any case, try to provide automatic changeover from heating to cooling, to minimize personal attention.

This is a broad program, long term, and without specifics. The specifics arise as you survey each system. There is no quick fix. With such a long-term program and the benefits that arise from it, you should be able to approach your supervisors for extra funds.

To respond directly to one of your comments: you are correct that the system with no extra components usually works best. Any clutter that you can eliminate should be advantageous. Just be *sure* it is nonessential.

A central computer-based control system (EMCS) is not mentioned. The steps outlined above should always precede any decision to install an EMCS. Usually, where all these steps are implemented, the value of an EMCS becomes marginal. You might want to consider DDC (direct digital control) as a replacement for some of the larger and more complex pneumatic and electronic systems. Costs are competitive, and there are several suppliers of good equipment.

I hope I've said something useful here. I repeat: it's not easy. But if you have a plan and carry it out as time and funds allow, good things can happen faster than you expect.

*   *   *

The correspondent read the answer, developed a plan, and went to his supervisor. I got a nice letter from the base commandant, thanking me for my assistance. The foreman got approval and began implementing a plan that included developing standard panels for typical units — single-zone, multizone, dual-duct, etc. A year later, this gentleman showed up at an ASHRAE professional development seminar at which I was a lecturer. He introduced himself and showed me pictures of the standard panels being manufactured and installed by his people. A very satisfactory ending!

Functions and communication in a control hierarchy*

Engineers tend to be pragmatic and practical: "Just show me how to fix it and don't bother me with a lot of theory!"

But theory — the reasons why it works or does not work — is essential if you are to solve the next control problem and the next and. . . .

The process control people are way ahead in this area; at least, if *Control Engineering* magazine represents the typical attitude of the process control engineer. I find the control theory expounded there very applicable to HVAC, though the details, of course, are different.

A recent advertisement in that magazine by a leading manufacturer of process controls was very interesting. The full-page ad included an exposition of the manufacturer's philosophy of function and communication in a hierarchical control system. Interestingly, computers are not mentioned, although the writer apparently took it for granted that a computer would be used to implement the philosophy in an efficient way.

With acknowledgment to the source, I'd like to paraphrase, in HVAC terms, some of the ideas in that advertisement. Figure 1-5 illustrates the general arrangement of the systems and functions.

Functions

Most people tend to think of the control system as having only two essential functions: monitoring and control. The ad suggests that a computer-based supervisory system has at least six functions:

---

*February 1985.

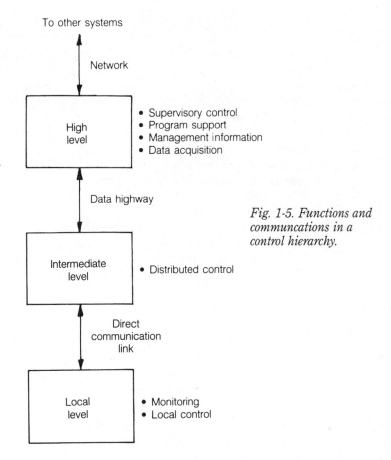

Fig. 1-5. Functions and communcations in a control hierarchy.

1. *Monitoring* is the first and essential function since, without it, there can be no adequate control.
2. *Distributed control* refers to the local-loop systems, including direct digital controllers, and to the supervisory functions performed by intelligent field-interface devices (IFID). This type of control is said to be event-driven and provides immediate response to the needs of the process (HVAC system) being controlled.
3. *Supervisory control* refers to the activities of the higher-level system, which oversees the activities of the FIDs and local loops, noting alarms and other out-of-control situations. In HVAC the system would be referred to as the central console. The operator can use the information received there to respond with corrective actions. In some cases the response might be automatic.
4. *Data acquisition* is similar to monitoring. The terms are used interchangeably in HVAC. The distinction suggested here is that data are acquired by accessing an online database relating to the process. In any

computer-based system, a database provides information about the various points connected to the system. While these data are normally fixed, they can vary from time to time because of changes made by the operator. In *adaptive* control they can be varied by the adaptive programs. In some facilities data may be acquired from other systems, such as fire and security.

5. *Program support* provides all of the program input and maintenance, including downloading, uploading, storage, modification, and verification of programs.

6. *Management information* refers to the assembly of data into report forms for management use. It can include history, trends, energy consumption, and maintenance-scheduling.

These six functions go far beyond traditional concepts of control and illustrate the expansion of those concepts brought about by the computer.

Communications

Linking all of these functions into an operating system requires not one but several communication systems:

1. Low-level communications between the FID (field-interface device) or DDC (direct digital control), and the local loop device are usually *direct*: wires or tubing link one device to another. Either analog or digital data can be handled easily and with high reliability.

2. Between the FID or DDC and the central console the communication link is a *data highway*. This link uses serial digital transmission and requires a formal message structure (*protocol*) for addressing and verification. The speed of response is related to the size of the system and the volume of traffic on the highway. Because of its greater complexity and dependence on several variables this link is not as reliable as the direct link, though reliability is high with present-day equipment.

3. At the highest level, connections between the central console and other computer systems are called *networks*. In some instances the network might allow one master system to control others or a backup system to take over if the primary system fails. Generally, the network is an information-transfer system. Networks are very useful but are not simple to implement. There are complex problems of priorities, communication control, and interpretation to be solved.

The process control people might be somewhat ahead of the HVAC people in applications, but the concepts discussed here are inherent in state-of-the-art, HVAC computer-based control systems. If the HVAC industry has not taken full advantage of them, it is more from lack of understanding of the potential available.

*   *   *

This is another good example of the rule that "technology changes but fundamentals do not." The theory discussed is still very valid, though not all of the protocol problems have been solved. These concepts are being used more frequently in HVAC.

Back to basics*

There is a need for an understanding of and a return to control fundamentals. In the mad rush to get aboard the technology train many tend to feel that some "newest and greatest" product is the solution to all control problems. It isn't.

The best control device will not work if it is improperly applied. Remember all the problems in the early days of EMCS? Too many overly enthusiastic salesmen thought that the computer was going to revolutionize the control industry. Several years and several hundred disillusioned customers later, some of the people went back to basics, and then the EMCS began to be an effective tool.

The basic principle to emphasize is that all control systems are built upon simple, elementary control loops. No matter how complex the final system might appear and no matter what sophisticated (or unsophisticated) techniques are used, the simple loop must always be there.

The elements of a basic *closed-loop* control system are shown in FIG. 1-6. A *sensor* measures the status of the *controlled variable*—in this case the air stream temperature. The sensed value is transmitted to the *controller*, where

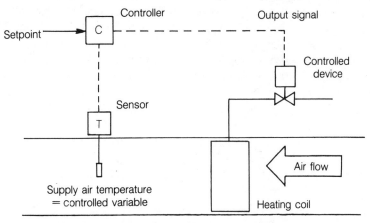

Fig. 1-6. Closed-loop control system.

---

*October 1985.

it is compared to a *setpoint*. This results in an output signal from the controller to the *controlled device*—in this example, a valve controlling the flow of heating fluid to a heating coil. A change in the output signal causes a change in the valve position, which causes a change in the flow of heating fluid and thus a change in the air stream temperature. The new temperature is sensed and transmitted to the controller, changing the output, etc. This is a closed loop because the change in the controlled variable caused by the control system is sensed by the system—a process called *feedback*. The duct and heating coil make up the *process plant* to which the control system is applied.

In an *open-loop* system, the sensed variable is not the controlled variable so there is no feedback. An example of this is control of boiler hot water temperature based on outdoor air temperature.

The example shown in FIG. 1-6 uses a familiar, simple HVAC system to make the explanation easier to follow. In control theory, a *block diagram* is used (FIG. 1-7). The blocks indicate the various elements in the control loop. Labels are added to the blocks to show that the two diagrams are equivalent.

By now most of you are saying, "This is old stuff. When is he going to tell us something new?"

Well, what is new to many of you is that the above dissertation includes probably 90 percent of all you need to know about control fundamentals. If you understand, really understand, what constitutes a control loop and how it works, you can understand any control system. Technology changes, fundamentals do not.

Many loops are not as simple and clear cut as the above example. It takes some analysis to sort out the overlays—bells and whistles—and find the basic elements. But they are always there.

For example, look at the typical economy cycle outside air control system in FIG. 1-8. There are actually two control loops involved, plus a fixed-output minimum position control. The normal closed loop consists of mixed air temperature sensor T3, controller C1, and damper operators M1, M2, and M3. This loop functions so long as the switching relay R2 allows the signal from C1 to pass to the high-signal selector relay R1 and so long as that signal is greater than the signal from the minimum position switch SW1. When the outside air temperature, as sensed by T2, is above the setpoint of controller C2, relay R2 is switched to block the signal from C1. (This is an example of two-position,

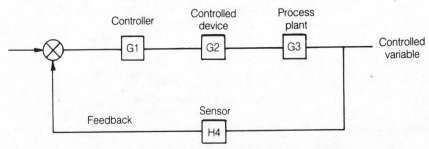

Fig. 1-7. Block diagram—closed-loop control system.

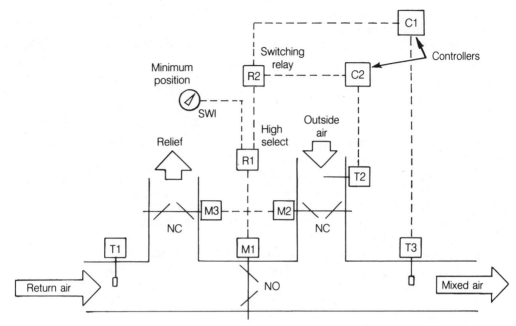

Fig. 1-8. Economy cycle outside air control.

open-loop control.) Then the signal from the minimum position switch becomes the high signal at relay R1 and controls the damper operators. Minimum position is also a control loop, in which the human operator has established the controller output.

This economy cycle appears somewhat complex at first glance, but it is much more understandable when reduced to its component loops. This type of analysis can be applied to any control system. Keep in mind that each loop must be complete; if any elements are missing, there will be no control. To understand any control system, reduce it to its essentials.

Research needs in HVAC*

At an NSF (National Science Foundation) workshop on research needs in HVAC systems, education was an urgent topic — particularly HVAC education at the college and university level. Educators agree that there are very few courses available in HVAC. A few schools have architectural engineering curricula (including HVAC) that emphasize the systems so necessary to the HVAC engineer. A few mechanical engineering curricula include perhaps one course in HVAC and refrigeration. Thus, most HVAC engineers get their

---

*May 1986.

HVAC training on the job, with widely varying results. More money for HVAC research might strengthen HVAC curricula.

The workshop groups developed research topics in the areas of equipment sizing and performance, computer use for design and analysis, and controls. The group on controls developed a list of twelve items, some of which are discussed here.

1. *Cost-benefit ratios,* for various types of control devices and control strategies. Some real numbers, based on independent research, would have more credibility than manufacturer's claims.
2. *Dynamics of subsystems.* Almost nothing is known about the response times of the various components of HVAC systems and controls. For example, what is the response time of a simple heating coil in an air stream following a change in the flow rate or temperature of the heating fluid? There are many such questions but almost no answers.
3. *Subsystem interactions.* The typical HVAC system includes a number of subsystems, each with its own independent control loop. For example, a VAV system can include control loops for outside air economy cycle, discharge air temperature, and fan speed to maintain duct static pressure and many variable-volume terminal units. Although each of these systems is theoretically independent they are, in fact, interactive through the air system. A change in the control point or controllability of one system can upset the other systems. Something about the dynamics of these interactions must be known to develop some strategies for feeding information — and using it — from one subsystem to another. You need to know if such complex procedures are cost effective.
4. *Adaptive control, predictive control, expert control and diagnostics.* Although listed as separate items, these all have a common thread. The idea here is to provide the kind of control that adapts to changes in load, climate and other operating conditions to operate the HVAC system at the maximum possible efficiency at all times. Research is needed to develop the needed algorithms. This is not a new idea and process control system designers have used it for some time. About 30 years ago, a new power generating station was built in Dallas. The plant had two units, each with boiler, turbine, and generator. To test the adaptive-control philosophy, the owner and designers provided detailed instrumentation and indication on both units. On one unit they also provided an automatic adaptive control system. On the other they provided for manual adjustment of system parameters by skilled operators. Apparently the algorithms they used were very good, because when the plant was placed in operation it became a challenge for the operators to keep up with the automatic system. They did not make it, always being one or two percentage points behind in operating efficiency. So the philosophy of adaptive or expert control is sound and probably cost effective. It also takes away some of the operator's

responsibility, as well as the understanding of the system — unless the operator is exceptional.

5. *Thermal storage* systems are popular. To design and operate such systems in the most efficient manner, it is necessary to use adaptive/ predictive controls. Research is needed to develop algorithms and innovative concepts.

6. *Control strategies.* There are probably better control strategies that can be used, given the proper tools. Most designers do not have the time or money to do the research and, especially, to determine which strategies would be the most cost effective and usable in specific situations.

7. *Air quality.* Control systems are important in control of air quality. Use of outside air, recirculation of cleaned return air, and other strategies are used. Very little work has been done in the area of sensing contaminants, although many sensors are available.

8. *Rating vs. field performance.* Any of you who have tried to start up an HVAC system and get it to perform as rated know that field performance and rated performance are not the same. In part, this is true because field conditions and geometry seldom, if ever, match the laboratory conditions prescribed by the testing and rating standards. Achieving design performance in the field requires a great deal of patience, adjustment, and understanding. There is some empirical understanding of the effect of geometry on the performance of system components, but almost no real data. What happens to a fan and coil combination when the coil is close to the fan inlet or outlet? What happens to the pressure losses in a duct system when the air flow is varied, as in VAV? There is plenty of room for research here. These variations affect the system gains which, in turn, affect control performance.

You might have some other suggestions. As you can see, there is a great deal that is not known about how HVAC systems work.

* * *

Very little has changed in the past few years. The research outlined here is costly and often difficult. Some of it is going on quietly, and hopefully there will be some usable results. There are many opportunities for enterprising people.

Research, theory, practice*

Research, theory, design, construction, and operation are five aspects of an HVAC control system (or any other system).

Each of these is important. The proper functioning of all is essential for optimum performance. Yet, how many people, each in a private little niche, takes the credit for a good system and blames others for the failures? Be honest about it: each thinks his or her area is the most important and fails to recognize the need for communication and education that will link all aspects together to make a system that really works as intended.

Theory is "what you learn in college," or part of what Doug Hittle and I talk about in the ASHRAE professional development seminars. And "everybody knows" that professors and college graduates have learned all that theory but "don't know anything practical." I was one of the everybodies for many years and properly superior to the impractical theorist. When I finally went to college, one of the most impressive things was learning how the theory tied all that practical experience together. I found out why some things worked and how others things could be done much better. For that matter, I'm still going through this process! And so I began to see, dimly, a relationship between theory and practice. It should be noted that control theory was not offered at my college. I had to learn by self study.

After college, I went to work as a designer of HVAC systems and controls. In the then small office of Bridgers and Paxton, I was fortunate enough to be expected to design both systems and controls. There are many large offices with control specialists, creating still another separate compartment. This might be efficient in terms of production, but too much specialization adds more communication problems to those that already exist.

It quickly became evident that the plans and specifications that went out of our office were not enough to get the system to function as we envisioned it. The installer seldom understood any of the theory, so he interpreted every document in terms of his past experience. After all, "That guy in the office who designed this system obviously does not understand how things work, so I'll have to fix it." Each of us has his own bit of superiority—reasonable, but fatal if carried to extremes. So we appreciated the installers who called us out to the job site to explain our design errors/deficiencies/foul-ups. Some times we were able to broaden their horizons; other times they broadened ours.

It was during this same period that I began to appreciate the problems of the operator. Bridgers and Paxton had a policy that included some of what we today call *commissioning*, along with some basic training for the operators. Typically, in six months to a year, we would receive a call from the owner saying that the company had a new operator and "How do we operate this HVAC system?" Documentation and written instructions, if they ever existed,

*August 1986.

had been lost. My sympathies are all with the operator when we say, "Keep the system design simple because the operator will reduce it to his or her level of understanding." What else is the operator to do when no one says anything? I have found that most operators can do it as planned when they know what the plan is. Not too many years ago one of our clients asked us to produce a set of as-built control diagrams and operating instructions. The need arose because the chief operator was about to retire and had all the information on file — in his head. Our survey disclosed that even the diagrams of the contractor who had been doing the maintenance on the controls for 20 years were inaccurate and incomplete. This situation is typical. It is the unusual owner who has good documentation.

Research is what those guys in the ivory towers do! That is the wrong impression most have. In fact, research is what anyone does when there is a question that needs an answer. The designer or operator who has a bright idea for a new control strategy and tries it out on a project is a researcher. Unfortunately, the designer can seldom determine the true result because of extraneous factors over which the designer has no control. That is why the laboratory, usually in the academic surrounding, is so important. When all the parameters can be controlled, then the effect of the varied parameter can be verified. Another thing to remember about research is that results must be in agreement with the known laws of physics. To quote Doug Hittle: "In our research, the best thing we do is prove again the first law of thermodynamics: the gazinta must equal the gazouta." I am occasionally asked to review a paper presenting an ingenious suggestion in HVAC or control design. Many of these propositions are very good, but it is amazing how blithely some of the proponents put forward arguments that conflict with physical laws, destroying the credibility of a good proposal.

To summarize: all the aspects of systems — research, theory, design, construction, and operation — are essential to obtaining a properly functioning system. Education is needed to remove the partitions separating the boxes and to utilize the abilities and contributions of people in all these areas.

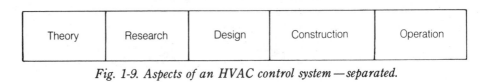

Fig. 1-9. Aspects of an HVAC control system — separated.

Fig. 1-10. Aspects of an HVAC control system — combined.

Instrumentation for control systems*

Instrumentation includes those devices that indicate the status of various items in the HVAC and control systems, such as air and water temperatures, valve and damper positions, operational status of motors, etc.

The criteria for selecting and specifying indicating instruments are the same as for other control devices: accuracy, reliability, maintainability, and credibility. Also, indicating devices fall into the familiar categories of analog and digital.

One of the major difficulties, especially in older systems, is the lack of credibility of the indicating devices. Credibility depends on the same quality of sensing needed for the monitoring use of the automatic control system. In most electronic control systems, the same sensor can be used for both input to the controller and input to the information display. TABLE 1-1 lists traditional and recommended ways of providing some of the more common information items.

For example, I prefer a platinum RTD (resistance temperature detector) with a digital readout meter for temperature. When combined with a manual selector switch, one meter can provide readout for several sensing points. Two-position indication—on/off, open/closed, flow/no flow—is usually pro-

Table 1-1. Sensing/Indicating Devices on Control Panels

Function	Traditional Methods	Recommended Methods
Temperature	1. Pneumatic sensor and indicator 2. Remote bulb and capillary with dial at panel 3. Thermocouple and meter 4. Remote sensor with recording meter	1. RTD sensor with digital readout on panel 2. Chilled mirror dew point sensor with digital readout at panel 3. Recorder if needed
Pressure	1. Analog gauge with tubing to sensing points 2. Remote contact sensor with light on panel	1. Same 2. Same
Humidity	1. Pneumatic sensor and indicator 2. Remote sensor/ transmitter with meter on panel	1. Solid-state or chilled mirror sensor/transmitter with meter on panel
Motor on/off	1. Auxiliary contact in starter with light on panel	1. Flow switch in duct or pipe, two lights on panel, with push-to-test function
Valve or damper position	1. Rheostat at device, meter at panel (analog) 2. Limit switch at device with light(s) on panel (digital)	1. Same 2. Same

*March 1987.

vided by means of *pilot indicating lights*. These lights are available in a wide range of sizes, types, colors and voltages. Make sure your selection is compatible with the rest of the system. Above all, do not make the mistake of mixing voltages in a control/indication panel. Always provide push-to-test buttons with pilot lights.

The purpose of instrumentation is to provide information for the guidance of the operator in analyzing problems and making control decisions. There might be problems with the HVAC system as well as with the controls. In fact, one of the things that good instrumentation shows is that many problems thought to be caused by controls are actually equipment and HVAC system problems. The information obtained by the operator will enable him or her to adjust the controls to compensate for the HVAC system inadequacies. The operator also will adjust the controls for maximum efficiency of operation, although this maximum might be limited by the HVAC system capability.

This gets us back to computer-based systems — EMCS and DDC. One of the advantages of these systems is the availability of operating data and the decision-making capability based on that information. An intelligent operator with equally good data can do the same things. For small systems, this method will probably be more cost effective.

Adequate data for the operation of any system are essential to understanding and diagnosing system problems. These data are only available through accurate and credible instrumentation systems. One valid piece of data is worth 100 educated guesses!

Solar heating effects*

The solar heating business has fallen off greatly since the demise of tax breaks and utility company rebates. Nevertheless, passive solar heating effects continue to be here, whether designed for or not. In particular, solar transmittance through glass has more effect than sometimes realized, and it can seriously affect HVAC design and system control.

Perhaps the most frequently overlooked phenomenon is the change in SHGF (solar heat gain factor) from summer to winter. Figure 1-11 shows the values for south facing glass at 40 degrees north latitude. Southern hemisphere data for north-facing glass are similar but slightly higher for summer and slightly lower for winter (with summer and winter months interchanged).

People in the southern hemisphere are used to making this adjustment. Notice that January values are 2½ to 3 times those for June because of the change in the tilt of the earth with respect to the sun.

The practical effect that this has on HVAC design and control is that, for a south-facing room or zone with 25 percent or more glass, the net heat gain on a mild January day might be greater than on a design day in June. This can

*April 1987.

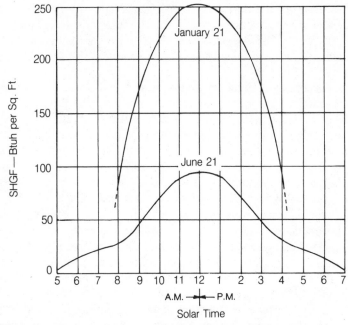

Fig. 1-11. Solar heat gain factors, south facing surface at 40 degrees north latitude.

result in undersizing the air supply and, if such south-facing areas are not provided with separate zoning, in loss of environmental control during parts of the winter. Overheating can easily occur.

Construction materials, glass type, shading, and other factors can influence the final result. Neglecting these factors can be hazardous to your design and control.

The following example is based on data in the *ASHRAE Handbook of Fundamentals*, 1985, chapters 23 through 27.

Assume a small office (part of a larger office building), south facing, in Cincinnati, Ohio (39 degrees north). The room is 10 by 10 by 9 feet high. The exterior wall has a total area of 90 square feet, of which 22.5 square feet are glass. The balance is insulated metal panel wall with a U-factor of 0.10. The glass is ¼-inch heat-absorbing glass, with interior drapes. The U-factor is 0.76, and the SC (shading coefficient) is 0.57.

At noon on June 21, the outside design temperature is about 90 degrees F, with an inside design temperature of 78 degrees F. At noon on January 21 the outside design temperature is about 22 degrees F, with inside design temperatures of 70 degrees F for heating and 78 degrees F for cooling. The SHGF at noon for June 21 is 95 Btuh per square foot; for January 21 it is 254 Btuh per square foot. The sol-air temperature difference on the south wall at noon June 21 is 39 degrees F. The CLF (cooling load factor) for this construction is 0.83. Detailed calculations are shown on page 33.

What these calculations show is that under some conditions the cooling load in a south facing zone might be greater in January than in June. This is particularly true in sunny, mild climates such as the Southwest.

Calculations

For June 21, the cooling load is:	Cooling
Glass (solar): 95 SHGF × 0.57 SC × 0.83 CLF × 22.5 sq ft =	1011 Btuh
Glass (conductance): (90 − 78)° F × 0.76 U × 22.5 sq ft =	205
Wall: 39 sol-air ΔT × 0.10 × 67.5 =	263
Lights: 200 watts × 3.41 Btuh per watt =	682
People (sensible): 1 × 250 =	250
Total	2411 Btuh

At an 18° F ΔT, this would require 124 cfm.

For January 21, the loads are:	Heating	Cooling
Glass (solar): 254 × 0.57 × 0.83 × 22.5 =		2703 Btuh
Glass (conductance): (70 − 22) × 0.76 × 22.5 =	821 Btuh	
Wall: (70 − 22) × 0.10 × 67.5 =	324	
Lights: 200 × 3.41 =		682
People (sensible): 1 × 250 =		250
Total	1145 Btuh	3635 Btuh

This results in a net cooling load of 3635 − 1145 = 2490 Btuh. At an 18 degrees F ΔT this would require 128 cfm. The sol-air effect has not been used in the wall heat loss. If it were, the wall ΔT would be 5 degrees F, for a heat loss of 34 Btuh and an increase in the net cooling load to 2780 Btuh, requiring 143 cfm.

Energy cost versus energy conservation*

The energy crisis might be over—temporarily, at least—but the continuing discussion about controlling the cost of energy is not. You are bombarded with suggestions: VAV, heat pumps, and thermal storage head the list. Solar energy, though sick, is by no means dead. Cogeneration is becoming the new buzz word. The power companies advertise special off-peak rates and special rates for all-electric buildings. All of these things reduce the cost of energy but do they really reduce energy consumption? You need to be aware that saving dollars and saving energy are not necessarily related.

---

*July 1987.

- *Heat pumps.* A heat pump utilizes heat energy already present in the ambient air, raising the temperature level mechanically to make the heat useful. The ratio of the amount of heat made available to the amount of electrical energy required to drive the heat pump is the COP (*coefficient of performance*). Some units have COP ratings of eight or more. But this high COP is only obtained at some relatively high ambient temperature. As the outside air temperature decreases and the heating load goes up, the capacity of the heat pump goes down. At outdoor air temperatures below 30 degrees F or so, supplemental heat is often needed—electrical resistance or other fuel. The *annual* or *seasonal COP* will be much less than the *rated COP*. Even so, the heat pump will save a great deal of energy on an annual basis. Because it takes no advantage of special rates and might even increase demand charges, its energy cost saving might not be as much as energy saved would predict.
- *VAV.* Variable-air volume systems save energy by varying the air flow rate as a function of load. VAV systems have been found to operate most of the time at 50 to 70 percent of design flow rate, with the maximum seldom exceeding 85 or 90 percent. In theory, fan horsepower varies as the cube of the change in air flow rate. In practice, the method by which the volume changes are accomplished governs the actual energy savings.

1. It is not practical to simply allow the composite of the VAV box damper actions to force the fan to "ride up the curve." This saves no energy and does make the system difficult or impossible to control, and it makes it noisy.
2. Mechanical variable-speed drives, belt-and-pulley or clutch type, are fine in theory. In practice there are often maintenance problems and always mechanical losses. Still, a large portion of the predicted energy savings might be obtained.
3. Inlet-vane dampers have, traditionally, been the preferred method of fan volume control. The inlet vane damper imparts a spin to the air entering the fan, thereby changing the fan performance characteristics. About half of the theoretical energy savings is obtained.
4. Electric, variable-frequency, variable-speed motor drives are now the preferred method of fan speed and volume control. Over the past few years, these devices have become more reliable and price competitive. The maximum possible energy savings should be obtained by this method. Even so, the reduction in motor efficiency at lower speeds means that the theoretical savings are not obtained. There may be problems with electrical interference due to generation of harmonics at certain speeds.
5. Small packaged systems for VAV are now being manufactured. These use run-around systems—bypass ducts with modulating dampers—for volume control so that air not needed by the VAV

boxes is bypassed back to the inlet side of the fan. The fan is, therefore, constant volume and no energy is saved. The justification made for this is that these are small systems and must be price competitive.

For all these systems the *mode* of the volume controller can be important. It has been shown that PI (proportional-plus-integral) control mode is superior to P (proportional-only) mode in energy savings. This is because of the inherent offset (control point error) of P control, which becomes greater as the load (air volume) decreases. Energy cost savings will not be as good as energy savings because fan power, even when reduced, will still tend to peak during maximum demand periods.

- *Thermal storage.* The philosophy here is to store hot or chilled water or ice in a reservoir at periods of low energy use for use at periods of high demand. This saves energy cost by taking advantage of off-peak rates and minimizing demand charges. In the cooling mode more energy is actually required than with a conventional non-storage system. This is because the chiller energy, in kilowatts per ton, increases as the chilled water temperature decreases, with ice storage aggravating this effect. There are also additional thermal losses/gains through piping and storage tank walls because of the lower (higher) temperatures. The cost of the energy is less because of the lower off-peak rates and demand charges.

The point of this discussion is to remind you that energy cost and energy use are not directly related. Look at all the factors involved. Are you really concerned with energy conservation or with dollar conservation?

*   *   *

Of course you are concerned with both. And there are some other related factors, such as: if you do not take advantage of off-peak rates and try to reduce demand, the power companies will have to build more plants, which will use more energy, etc. Nothing is simple. Always analyze to determine the most cost- and energy-effective alternative for the long term.

Comfort: forgotten factor in economic analysis*

This discussion concerns the economics of first cost and operating cost in commercial, industrial and institutional buildings. Some economic aspects are considered that are not usually seen as being related but, in my opinion, should be included in the cost analysis.

---

*September 1988.

Present-day energy codes require that buildings and systems be designed, at least theoretically, to limit energy consumption. Operating and control strategies have a great deal of influence on the actual energy consumption and the environment in the building. The HVAC equipment and control devices selected and installed also affect both these factors.

The purpose of an HVAC system is to provide a suitable environment for the people and processes in the building. In an attempt to save money, this fundamental consideration is often overlooked by designers, owners, and operators. But, it is the key to the real economic problem.

The real economic problem is neither the first cost nor the operating cost of the HVAC system, although obviously these are important. The real problem is the effect the environment has on people and processes. Anything that degrades the environment can have an adverse effect on the economic situation.

This is more readily understood by considering the process environment. A very common example in present-day practice is the manufacturing of electronic chips. The process requires a clean-room environment with very close control of temperature and humidity. With a daily production output worth up to half a million dollars, the manufacturer is not greatly concerned above the HVAC system cost but only with its accuracy and reliability. Efforts might be made to limit first and operating costs, but they are always subordinated to the needs of the process. The economics of this situation are fairly obvious.

In the world of the commercial office building, where the primary requirement is to provide a suitable environment for the office worker, the economics are not so obvious and are often—usually—ignored. Nevertheless, there are some interesting observations that can be made.

First cost of the HVAC system can vary widely, depending on quality and complexity. Most economic analyses consider only the life-cycle cost of the system—the effects that quality and operating strategy have on life, maintenance, and energy consumption. Typical operating utility costs are in the range of $2 to $3 per square foot per year. If an average occupancy of one person per 100 square feet is assumed, the annual utility cost per person is about $300 per year. It does not seem unreasonable to assume an average salary (including fringe benefits) of $30,000 per year per worker.

Now, if in the interest of energy conservation the thermostat settings are decreased in winter and increased in summer to the margins of the comfort zone, this might save, at most 10 to 20 percent of the energy cost. If, as a result, the average worker loses one percent of his or her productivity, that cost saving has been more than negated. Conversely, if worker productivity can be increased one percent by the ideal environment, the entire annual utility cost can be offset.

There are few, if any definitive studies linking productivity to environment. Several were attempted by ASHRAE many years ago, but the results were inconclusive. There are some fairly accurate, though necessarily subjective, definitions of comfort (see the *ASHRAE Handbook—Fundamentals*,

1985, chapter 8). These definitions are useful in selecting design and initial operating conditions. However, the uncomfortable worker is not only distracted from his own work but also loses no opportunity to complain to his boss and co-workers. Thus, an estimate of one percent loss of productivity does not seem unreasonable.

Having said all this, what conclusions can be drawn? It seems reasonable that you should treat the comfort environment with the same respect and economic consideration that you give the process environment. The owner is interested in the maximum return on investment. All of the factors affecting that investment should be considered. Therefore, savings due to marginal operation and maintenance of HVAC and other building systems must be measured against their effects on productivity as well as system life and reliability. Almost always these factors are ignored.

Like most problems in building use, this problem is one of education and communication. The designer must educate him or herself and, in turn, communicate that knowledge to the building owner and operator.

Part 2

Theory

Theory includes a great deal in HVAC controls. It covers not only control theory in the classical sense but also HVAC design principles. You cannot design controls in a vacuum. There is an essential relationship among all the system elements in a facility: the building, the process within the building with its environmental requirements, the HVAC systems, and finally, the control system. If any of these elements is deficient, there will be failure to some degree. So theory includes not only the technical but also a healthy dose of philosophy. It is difficult to separate philosophy from theory, and to be safe, look in both sections, as well as the rest of the book!

The successful control designer must have a broad understanding of the contribution of all elements to the overall system—the designer must be a generalist, a true systems engineer. But you cannot get there all at once. You learn a bit at a time through study, mistakes, and successes.

Each of the pieces in this section covers a small, specific topic. Together, they begin to add up, but this is hardly a complete story. You need much more, but you will find these odds and ends helpful.

Control of cooling/dehumidifying coils*

The designer of the HVAC control system must first understand how the elements of the HVAC system work. With that in mind, this discussion centers on the extended surface coil as used for cooling and dehumidifying.

In an extended surface or finned coil, the cooling medium — refrigerant, chilled water or brine — is contained within the tubes. Heat is transferred by conduction through the tube walls (primary surface) and the fins (secondary surface). Air impinging on these surfaces is cooled by convection. Condensation might take place if the surface temperature is below the dew point of the air.

Figure 2-1 illustrates the process. In this cross-sectional view, you can see that some of the air particles (indicated by arrows) impinge on the tubes or fins, and others pass through the coil untouched. Obviously, if more rows of tubes are used or if the fins were bent to increase turbulence, the fraction of air that is bypassed will be reduced.

In the coil there are several processes going on simultaneously. Part of the air is being cooled to saturation; then, as moisture condenses out, this air is further cooled down the saturation curve (State 2 in FIG. 2-2). The final saturation temperature is a function of the coil geometry and the entering water or refrigerant temperature; it is known as the ADP (*apparatus dew point*). Another fraction of air is bypassed and remains at the conditions of State 1. Other, relatively small, fractions of the air are presumably being cooled and dehumidified to various unknown states along the solid line process from 1 to 2.

From psychrometric theory it is known that a mixture of air from two conditions lies on a straight line connecting those two state points on the chart, with the length of the line segments inversely proportional to the air quantities.

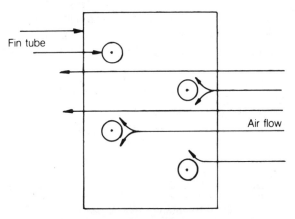

Fig. 2-1. Partial cross section of a finned coil.

*July 1980.

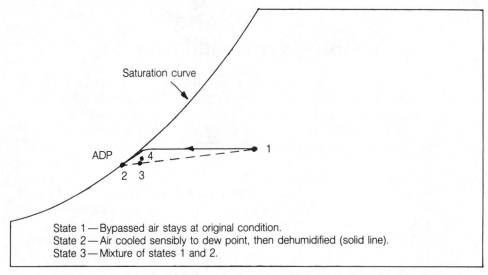

Saturation curve

ADP

4

1

2 3

State 1—Bypassed air stays at original condition.
State 2—Air cooled sensibly to dew point, then dehumidified (solid line).
State 3—Mixture of states 1 and 2.

Fig. 2-2. Psychrometric chart showing air flow through a cooling/dehumidifying coil.

Thus the mixture of States 1 and 2 could be at State 3. Because all other air fractions contribute to the mixture, the final condition is probably more like State 4.

The important idea here is that unless the bypass factor is very large, States 3 and 4 will be very close to the saturation curve. The typical cooling coil with four to eight rows of tubes usually has a bypass factor of five percent or less and will cool the air mixture to 95 percent relative humidity or even higher.

Figure 2-3 illustrates two impractical processes. The cooling process 1-2 is impossible because the condition line connecting state points 1 and 2 does not intersect the saturation curve. Therefore there is no APD (apparatus dew point). To get from point 1 to point 2, it is necessary to cool the air to a dew point equal to that of point 2 and then reheat (dotted lines). If that dew point is below freezing it may be impossible to do this and chemical dehumidification will be required. Process 1-3 implies a 50 percent bypass factor that can only be obtained with a one-row coil with wide fin spacing. It probably is not a real process and, in any case, would provide only sensible cooling (not dehumidification, as the figure implies).

What does all this mean in terms of control? If the psychrometric chart analysis is used, the control conditions and the controllability of the system can be readily determined.

In FIG. 2-4, a simple mixing/cooling/dehumidifying cycle, using typical design conditions, is shown. Room air at State 1 (78 degrees F dry bulb and 65 degrees F wet bulb) is mixed with outdoor air at State 2 (95 degrees F dry bulb and 78 degrees F wet bulb) to obtain a mixture at State 3 (82 degrees F dry bulb and 68.2 degrees F wet bulb). The cooling load sensible/total ratio determines the slope of the line 1-4. For this discussion, it is assumed to be 0.95. Point 4 is then as shown, at 58 degrees F dry bulb and 94 percent

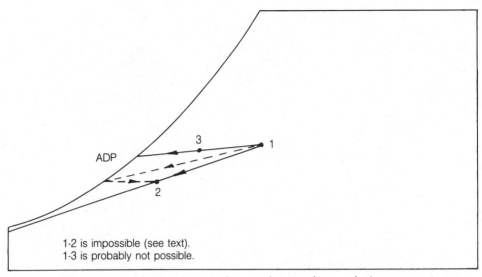

Fig. 2-3. Psychrometric chart illustrating two impractical processes.

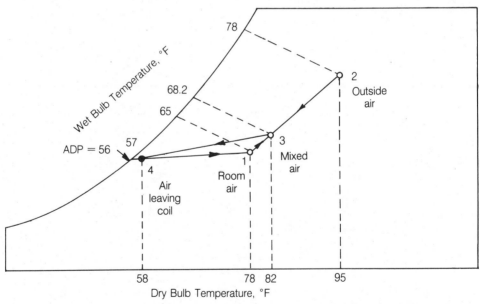

Fig. 2-4. Psychrometric chart illustrating a simple cooling/dehumidifying cycle.

relative humidity, which is quite reasonable for the normal bypass factor of a four- to six-row coil. The apparatus dew point is 56 degrees F, which could be obtained with entering water at 46 degrees F or even higher.

Note that this cycle requires the supply air quantity to be calculated using a 20 degrees F temperature difference (ΔT). If some smaller ΔT, such as 16 degrees F is to be used, then reheat will be required, as in FIG. 2-5, because the higher bypass factor is not practical. The result of a smaller ΔT without reheat would be to shift the cycle higher up on the chart, as in FIG. 2-6, with a resulting increase in room relative humidity; or the room temperature could be decreased, with a consequent increase in load.

This analysis shows us the conditions for control and controllability in the cycle. Many cycles are more complex than this but the principles remain the

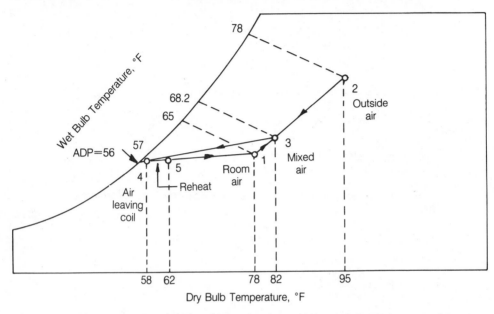

Fig. 2-5. Cooling and dehumidifying if supply air at 16 degrees F ΔT is used with reheat.

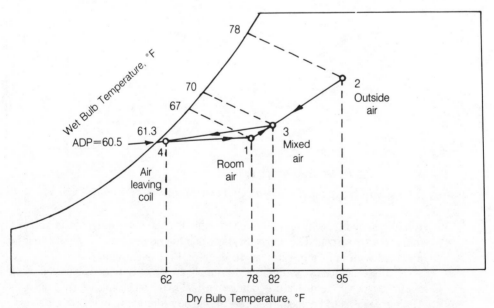

Fig. 2-6. Cooling and dehumidifying if supply air at 16 degrees FΔT is used.

same. There is no substitute for a psychrometric chart analysis in air conditioning system design.

* * *

This analysis considers only design load conditions. Some day I might write a follow-up article to show what happens at part load — which is the normal state of affairs in most applications. What happens when the chilled water flow is restricted to match a decrease in load? The coil capacity decreases and dehumidification will be decreased or eliminated. The system will probably end at some higher room humidity doing sensible cooling only, at which point the bypass factor becomes unimportant. It is an interesting exercise to work out on the psychrometric chart.

Control logic*

In general, the following is true: "If this condition exists, then we want that to happen." Analytical procedures of this type are used extensively in the process control industry and in EMCS optimizing programs. The procedure is simply a mechanical way of simulating the thought processes and analyses you go through in making a judgment. There is nothing really mysterious about it, but it forces you to arrange your data in an orderly, logical manner.

For example, use a system consisting of three HV (heating and ventilating) units with hot water being supplied from two boilers (one large and one small) with a total of three pumps, as shown in FIG. 2-7. To operate efficiently, you want to use the combination of boilers and pumps that is most suitable, based on the number of HV units in use and the outdoor temperature.

After a load analysis, you can come up with a logic table, TABLE 2-1. The accuracy with which this table matches actual operating conditions will determine the energy savings accomplished.

The precomputer method of implementing this logic was by means of electromechanical relays. For simple systems, this is still a valid method. Figure 2-8 shows how it is done. The line numbers and reference numbers allow you to locate related control relay coils and contacts easily. It takes some

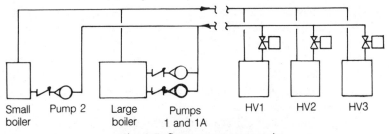

Fig. 2-7. System arrangement.

July 1982.

Table 2-1. Logic Table

Outdoor Temperature	Quantity of HV Units On	Boilers On	Pumps On
Below 70°F	1	Small	2
	2	Small	2 and 1A
Below 55°F	1	Small	2
	2	Large	1
	3	Large	1 and 1A
Below 40 °F	1	Small	2
	2	Large	1 and 1A
	3	Both	All

time to analyze all the relationships that exist, even in this simple system. As systems become more complex, it gets more difficult (exponentially). There are mathematical procedures available to assist in this; for example, Boolean algebra. Solid-state electronics designers often use AND-OR logic analysis.

This simple example uses 12 relays. It is beginning to get expensive — not the cost of the relays but the cost of wiring and interconnecting all those points. We can simplify the implementation by using a *process controller*. These devices, actually specialized microprocessors, are available in a wide variety of capabilities and prices. Most of them can be user programmed, using the logic exactly as shown in FIG. 2-8. Then the controller functions in exactly the same way as the group of relays. The advantages of the controller over the relays are that changes in the logic are easily reprogrammed, and no wiring changes are needed. Programming is a simple task, often requiring no knowledge of program language.

If the system shown in FIG. 2-7 is in a building that is part of a larger complex having a computer-based EMCS, the computer can be used to handle the logic. Engineers and designers are not expected to be programmers. Nevertheless, you can use the logic table to develop a *flow chart*, which the programmers can use to write the needed programs. The flow chart in FIG. 2-9 uses a special set of symbols to indicate the function involved in each step, but otherwise it simply expresses the logic process we've already been through.

This flow chart is a *subroutine*, which the computer will call up at regular intervals or when an HV unit is started. The database contains the latest data on temperatures and operating conditions of the various elements. The diamond shapes indicate a decision — yes or no — that causes the program to *branch* to an alternate course of action. The computer can only deal with *yes* or *no*. It cannot make judgments as the human mind does. Thus, it is necessary to reduce the judgment-making process to a series of yes or no statements.

The *start* processes are really additional subroutines involving a number

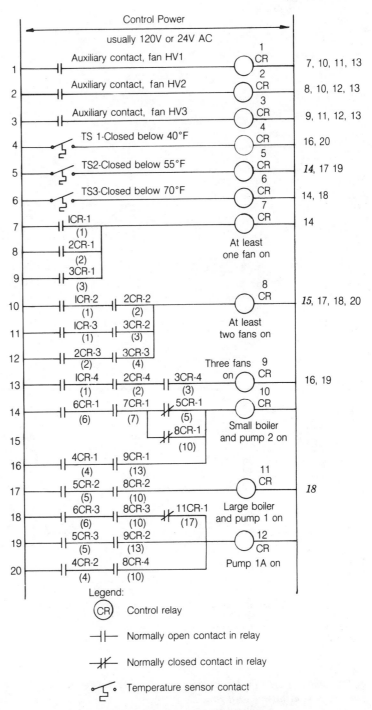

Fig. 2-8. Electrical logic diagram.

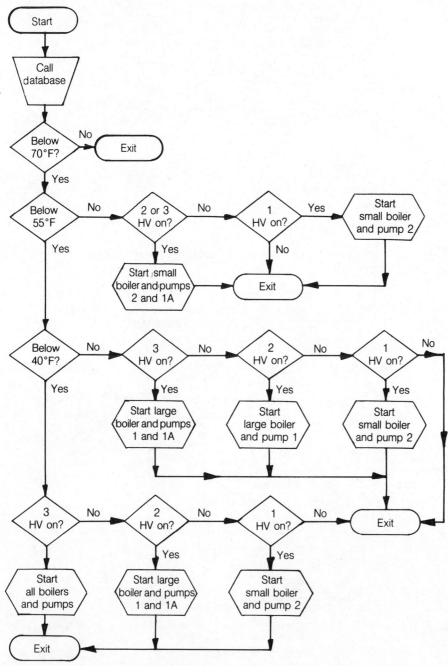

Fig. 2-9. Flow chart. Temperatures are outdoor temperatures. HV refers to heating and ventilating unit fan.

of steps, such as identifying the correct point, checking status, closing contacts, checking to see that the device really started, etc.

The details of all these sequences might appear a bit complicated, but careful study will reveal the logic. You might even see some other (better?) way to proceed. At any rate, if you can follow these descriptions and then go on to develop similar material for your own problems, you can become a systems analyst. Congratulations!

For further study in logical analysis, find a control text or articles that discuss Boolean algebra.

*   *   *

This is a good example of the rule that technology changes but fundamentals do not. Since this was written, there have been some considerable advances in technology. Today you could use a DDC rather than a programmable controller, though they are not all that different in principle. Programming has become much simpler with the use of interactive software and many standard subroutines. The principles discussed in this article have not changed. The analysis still must be made and the logic table is still the simplest way to understand and implement it.

Proportional-plus-integral control*

The typical modulating pneumatic controller used with HVAC systems is a P (*proportional*) type controller. In a closed-loop system, FIG. 2-10, a sensor provides information on the value of a *controlled variable* (the air stream temperature in this illustration). This value is compared in the controller with a *setpoint* and the difference is read as an *error*. The error is multiplied by

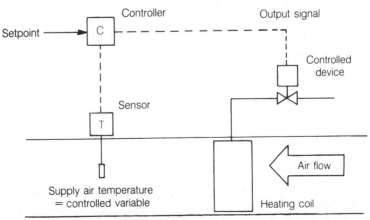

Fig. 2-10. Closed-loop control system.

*January 1984.

a constant called the *gain* to obtain an output. The output is used to position a *controlled device* (a valve in the illustration) that will cause a change in the controlled variable to return its value to the setpoint. This is expressed mathematically as:

$$Q = A + K_p e \qquad\qquad (2\text{-}1)$$

where: Q = controller output
A = constant equal to controller output with no error
K_p = proportional gain constant
e = error

The gain is the reciprocal of the *throttling range*, the range of controller output over which the controlled device modulates from one extreme to the other. A typical throttling range in a pneumatic system is 10 psi (pounds per square inch)—3 to 13 psi. If the differential of this controller is 4 degrees F, then the gain is 10/4 or 2.5 psi per degree F. This means that for every degree of error, the controller output will vary 2.5 psi from the neutral point (usually 8 psi).

For any control system, a sudden change in the set point or the value of the controlled variable will result in an *upset*. The time the system takes to respond is a function of several variables: sensor, controlled device, coil response, and controller. The result is shown in FIG. 2-11. The figure illustrates a sudden increase in setpoint (or decrease in controlled variable). The control system responds by opening the valve, increasing the air temperature. *Overshoot* occurs as the air temperature rises above the setpoint.

The controller reacts by partially closing the valve, and the air temperature decreases—again with overshoot. Figure 2-11 shows a *stable* system, with steady state being reached after a few cycles. Notice that the steady state value of the controlled variable will not match the setpoint. This *offset* is an inherent characteristic of proportional control and can be either plus or minus, depending on the circumstances. If the system is unstable, steady state equilibrium will not be obtained, and the system will cycle indefinitely (*hunt*) as shown in FIG. 2-12. Instability is usually caused by a too high gain (narrow throttling range) and can usually be corrected by decreasing the gain. However, a too low gain can cause the system to respond sluggishly with an increase in the steady state offset.

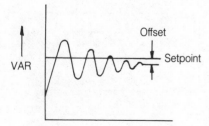

Fig. 2-11. Proportional control—stable.

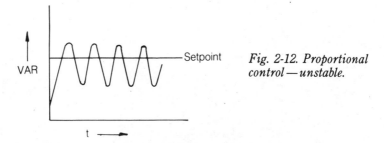

Fig. 2-12. Proportional control — unstable.

As noted, offset is an inherent property of proportional control. The reason for this is illustrated in FIGS. 2-13 and 2-14. In FIG. 2-13, the water tank level is at the setpoint as determined by the float level sensor and float valve. Water is flowing in and out at X gallons per minute. If the exit valve is opened wider so that X plus ΔX gallons per minute flows out (increase in load), the water level will drop until the valve opens wide enough to allow X plus ΔX to flow in (FIG. 2-14). The system will stabilize at this new condition with an offset probably less than ΔX.

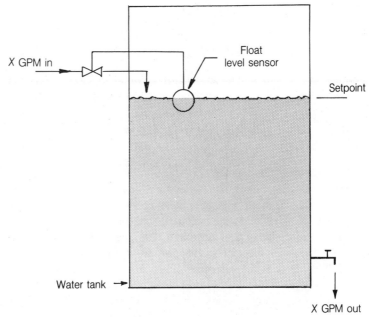

Fig. 2-13. Water tank — initial flow rate.

In many HVAC systems, offset is not a serious problem and might even conserve energy. For example, in a heating system, offset might cause the control point to be lower than the setpoint, resulting in a decrease in heating load. However, in VAV (variable air volume) systems, the static pressure control point will tend to increase as load (air quantity) decreases, resulting in an increase in fan work (see reference 3 at the end of this section).

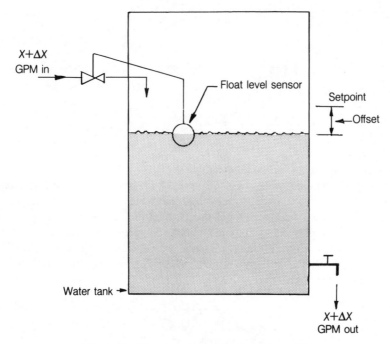

Fig. 2-14. Water tank—change in flow rate.

To minimize or eliminate offset, PI (*proportional-plus-integral*) control is used. This control mode adds a second term to the control equation, thus:

$$Q = A + K_p e + K_i \int e dt \qquad (2-2)$$

where: K_i = integral gain constant.

The integral term means that the error is being measured at regular and frequent intervals and that the sum of these measurements, multiplied by the integral gain, is being added to the output. Thus, the longer the error persists, the greater the response of the controller. The effect of this is equivalent to resetting the controller setpoint so that the offset from the initial setpoint is eliminated. The result is the response shown in FIG. 2-15, which is similar to that of FIG. 2-11 but with no offset. PI control is often called *reset* control, though the term is technically incorrect.

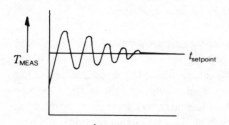

Fig. 2-15. Proportional-plus-integral control.

PI control provides a high degree of accuracy. With PI control, it is possible to use a very small proportional gain (wide throttling range) for stable control and still get rapid, accurate response. However, an integral gain that is too high can also result in instability.

Proper adjustment of both proportional and integral gains must be done in the field by experienced people, because the response times of many HVAC system elements are not known. While most present-day electronic controllers include both P and PI functions, it is also possible to add PI capability to a pneumatic system.

References

1. ASHRAE Professional Development Seminar No. 2, "Automatic Temperature Controls for Energy/Cost Effectiveness."

2. G. Shavit, and S. Brandt, "Dynamic Performance of a Discharge Air-Temperature System with a PI Controller," ASHRAE Journal, September 1982.

3. R.W. Haines, "Supply Fan Volume Control in a VAV System," in part 3 of this book.

System Gains*

As noted in the section on PI control, a high gain can result in unstable control, and a low gain can produce slow response. This section covers *system* gains. The gain due to HVAC component and system design can have the same effect as the controller gains on the controllability of the system. System gains are major factors in the system control problem.

System gains occur when the response of the system components to a change in output is nonlinear — that is, the response is greater or less than the change in controller output would lead you to expect.

To illustrate this, look again at the basic closed-loop system diagram (FIG. 2-16). System gains are related to the control valve, the heating coil, the hot water supply temperature, the air stream, and the interaction among those elements.

Control valve

The factors affecting control valve response and gain are size and type. Control valve size is determined by the fluid flow rate and allowable pressure drop. Flow rate is, of course, a function of design heat-transfer capacity and design water temperature drop. Valve pressure drop should be approximately

---

*February 1984.

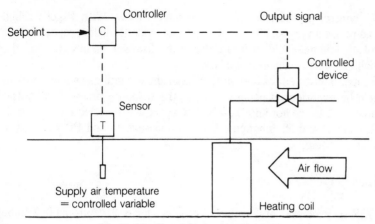

Fig. 2-16. Closed-loop control system.

equal to that in the coil and the branch piping system serving the coil — usually in the order of 10 to 20 feet wc (4 to 8 psi). The following equation is then used to determine the design valve sizing factor:

$$C_v = Q/(H)^{1/2} \qquad (2\text{-}3)$$

where: C_v = valve sizing coefficient
Q = design flow (gallons per minute or pound per hour)
H = design pressure drop, psi

By consulting a manufacturer's catalog, a valve of approximately the correct size can be selected, noting that design C_v relates to the fully open position of the valve. In most cases, this will mean that the selected valve will have a wide-open C_v greater than required because there is not an infinite range of C_v ratings from which to select. Thus, immediately, the valve will be oversized, which means that for a given controller output — and valve position — the water flow will be greater than design. Also the available pressure drop will be greater than design because most pumps are selected to provide a minimum pressure differential at some remote point in the distribution system.

The other factor in valve selection is the type of plug used. It is usually advisable to use a proportional plug such that flow rate varies with plug lift (travel) in an exponential fashion, FIG. 2-17. With this type of plug there is a small change in flow rate for fairly large change in lift when the valve is nearly closed. This tends to offset the effects of oversizing and higher available pressure drop at light-load conditions. At medium- and high-load conditions, the valve might contribute a good deal to system gain.

Heat transfer coil

The coil is to provide some Btuh output for a given air flow rate, water flow rate and entering air and water temperatures. An interesting thing hap-

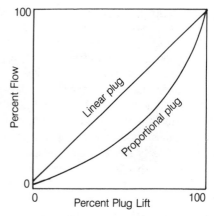

Fig. 2-17. Flow versus valve plug lift (travel) for two types of valve plugs.

pens as water flow rate is decreased. The temperature drop of the water increases and the coil output does not decrease in a linear way. In fact, it might decrease very little at first, as shown in FIG. 2-18. The location of the curve in this figure is mostly a function of the difference between the entering air and water and entering water temperatures. A lower ΔT results in a curve closer to linear. The simple way to minimize the problem is to reduce the entering water temperature to the lowest acceptable level. Then, if a proportional plug is used, the combination of valve curve and coil curve will approximate a linear response.

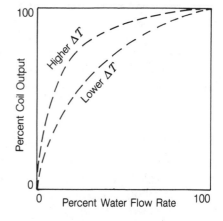

Fig. 2-18. Coil output as a function of entering water versus entering air temperatures.

This effect can be exaggerated if the air system is a VAV type because reduction of the air flow rate decreases the load but not at the same rate as it decreases the coil capacity. Now a smaller change in water flow rate will create a greater change in the air discharge temperature and, therefore, have a greater effect on the sensor and controller. It is difficult enough to deal with the system gain as the water flow rate varies but even more difficult if both water and air flow rates vary.

The common practice of oversizing the heating coil for safety can only lead to control problems and instability.

The control designer can minimize system gains by observing these criteria:

1. Avoid oversizing of heat exchanger coils and control valves. In marginal cases, it is probably best to undersize slightly because design conditions seldom occur.
2. Maintain supply water temperatures as close to entering air temperature as is practicable while still satisfying the building environment.
3. In most cases, use a proportional plug in the control valve. Use a linear plug only if it can be demonstrated that the system response will be linear (that is, when using steam).

If the system gains are minimized, the control system has a much better chance of providing stable operation.

Damper control gains are similar to valve gains and are usually due to oversizing. A smaller damper with a higher initial pressure drop will usually allow better control.

Hysteresis creates control problems that are similar to those caused by high gain but are actually caused by slow response. In pneumatic systems, positive positioners on valve and damper actuators is recommended. On all systems, linkages should have as little slack as possible and should be maintained in this condition.

*   *   *

Yes, reducing the entering water temperature might require more coil capacity. But most preliminary heating (and cooling) coil selection calculations result in a fractional number of rows. Then you can consider reducing the water temperature to get close to an even number of rows. Safety factors might make you feel more secure, but they can make accurate and stable control difficult.

Estimating energy consumption*

Numerous computer programs for estimating energy consumption in buildings are now available. This type of program is useful as a design tool because various combinations of building construction, HVAC types, and control strategies can be compared to determine energy costs and life cycle costs. The most economical system and control strategy can be selected.

These programs are available from many private and government sources. They share a common problem: the numbers obtained from the estimates are not real. That is, when the building is built and the systems are installed and operated, the actual energy consumption and cost might vary greatly from the estimates—as much as 50 percent.

---

*April 1984.

There are many reasons for this. First, the standard weather year used in most hour-by-hour simulations provides the necessary sequence of outdoor temperature for the calculations, but the temperatures encountered in use will not be the same.

A second reason relates to equipment efficiencies. The programs require that fan motor, boiler, and chiller efficiencies be input; it is assumed that these are constants, although chiller part-load efficiencies are sometimes used. Very few devices will match claimed efficiencies in the field, particularly on an annual basis. Regrettably, not all manufacturers provide 100 percent factory test quality control and, even then, field conditions seldom match those specified for laboratory or factory testing. Electrical power sources might not be perfect — undervoltage can decrease efficiency and capacity. This factor is usually overlooked by user and designer alike. How many specifications include efficiency test procedures? A difference of four or five percent in fan efficiency can result in hundreds of dollars of extra cost each year.

Another factor is the training and motivation of the building operators. A difference in attitude and training is hard to quantify, but it can easily result in a difference of 10 to 20 percent of annual energy consumption. (See reference 1 at the end of this section.) The computer program assumes that operation is always in accordance with appropriate schedules and control settings.

Finally, the HVAC system control strategies must be input to the computer program, which assumes that those strategies are followed and that setpoints and control points are accurately tracked. In the real world that is just not true. The typical proportional control system always has an offset between the setpoint and the actual control point. (See reference 2 at the end of this section.) This offset may be as much as four or five degrees F at light loads. According to a recent study a 5 degree F offset in mixed air temperature can result in an increase of 60 percent in annual cooling energy or 30 percent in annual heating energy. (See reference 3 at the end of this section.) Offsets in other temperatures, such as space or supply air, also can result in excessive energy usage. This is in general agreement with the variations in energy consumption obtained by inputting different setpoints to the program.

What does this mean to us as designers, contractors, or owners? Four ideas are important here:

1. Do not expect actual energy use in a building to match that estimated by using a computer program.
2. Do specify careful and comprehensive field testing to prove efficiencies and proper control operation.
3. Provide the best possible training and motivation for the operating staff.
4. Continually look for ways to improve operation and decrease energy use. Experience and historical data, properly used, should always lead to improvement.

References

1. William J. Toohey, "Saving Energy in Commercial Buildings," *Heating/Piping/Air Conditioning*, March 1982.

2. Roger W. Haines, "Proportional-Plus-Integral Control," in part 2 of this book.

3. James T. Kao and E. Thomas Pierce, "Sensor Errors: Effect on Energy Consumption," *ASHRAE Journal*, December 1983.

*   *   *

I've heard too many stories about energy savings through education to recount here, but the weight of evidence convinces me that an educated and motivated operating crew is much more important than any other factor in conservation of energy while maintaining the proper environment. My classic example is the Dallas Fort Worth Airport central plant operation, headed up by Al Utesch. In the first ten years of operation, the square footage of occupied space was approximately doubled while achieving a decrease in total energy use. Some of this was accomplished by making changes in equipment. The cost of those changes was amortized in about one year in all cases. The rest was simply the result of studying the result of changes in operating procedures and implementing the most efficient. It does not happen by accident!

Fan energy—proportional versus proportional-plus-integral control*

In another section of this book fan volume control for VAV systems is discussed. (See reference 1 at the end of this section.) It is suggested that PI (proportional-plus-integral) control would provide more fan energy savings than simple P (proportional) control. A typical question is "How does one quantify this energy saving in terms the owner can understand?"

The following discussion is an attempt to clarify the concept and provide a basis for quantifying the comparative energy consumptions.

Figure 2-19 shows the pressure profiles in a VAV system supply duct. At the top of the figure are shown the elements of concern: the supply fan, the static-pressure sensor, and controller, and a VAV box near the end of the system. Pressure is at a maximum at the fan discharge, gradually reducing down the length of the duct through friction and turbulence. For simplicity, a uniform reduction has been assumed, although that would not necessarily be true in a real system.

---

*August 1984.

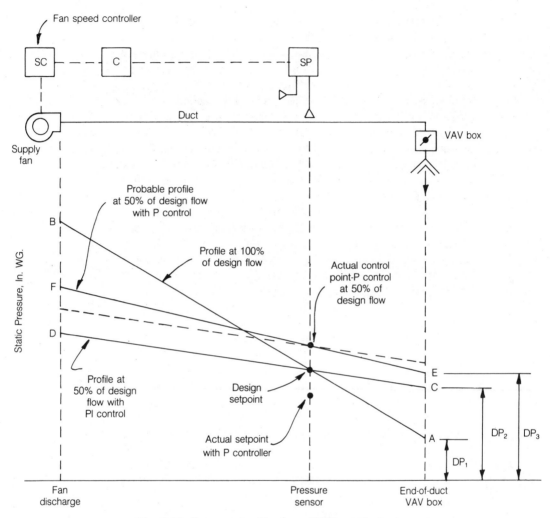

Fig. 2-19. Pressure profiles in a VAV supply duct.

The static-pressure sensor provides a signal to the controller, which adjusts the fan speed to maintain a constant static pressure at the sensor location. The pressure will remain constant with PI control but will not with P control, as shown in FIG. 2-20.

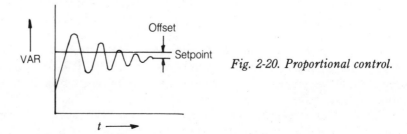

Fig. 2-20. Proportional control.

The VAV box contains a damper. The zone thermostat adjusts the damper to vary the air flow to the zone to match the load. The box usually includes a velocity sensor or mechanical device to compensate for variations in the duct static pressure at the box. The box and damper are analogous to a water or steam flow control valve, with a nonlinear damper constant similar to the C_v coefficient of the valve. (See reference 2 at the end of this section.)

The pressure controller is set to provide just enough pressure at design air flow rate to satisfy the end-of-the-duct VAV box. As the damper throttles to reduce air flow, the pressure drop across the damper and box increases. This is shown by the DP_1 and DT_2 indications in FIG. 2-19. DP_1 indicates the box pressure drop at design flow (damper open), and DP_2 indicates the pressure drop at reduced flow, say 50 percent.

Then, for a uniform pressure loss in the duct at design flow rate, the pressure profile will be as shown by line B–A. Note that this line passes through the design setpoint at the static pressure sensor. This setpoint will also be the control point with PI control. If P control is used, the setpoint must be lower to allow for the offset, as indicated. If the lower setpoint is not used, the profile with P control will have the same slope but will be higher at fan discharge and VAV box, requiring more fan horsepower and some throttling of the VAV damper.

As air flow is reduced, due to partial closing of the VAV dampers in response to decrease in load, the slope of the pressure profile will change. For illustration, a reduction to 50 percent of total air flow is assumed. Then, if the design static pressure control point is maintained (PI control), the profile will be shown by line D–C, with a reduction in fan horsepower and an increase in pressure drop across the VAV box. If P control were used, the resulting control point would be offset still higher and the profile would probably look like line F–E, with a somewhat higher pressure drop (DP_3) and flow across the VAV box. If the box were fully compensated for pressure changes, DP_3 would have a greater value, and the profile would follow the dashed line. In either case, the fan discharge pressure, and the fan horsepower would be greater than with PI control.

The meaning of this in terms of fan performance is shown in FIG. 2-21, which shows performance at various speeds for a typical, non-overloading, airfoil blade fan. Fan speed reduction produces a family of parallel curves, only a few of which are shown. You can also plot the curve showing system resistance as a function of air flow, remembering that pressure loss varies as the square of air flow rate change. At design flow rate, the fan selection point includes the system pressure loss plus the pressure drop across the VAV damper and box (DP). As the flow is reduced the fan runs more slowly, the system curve shows a decrease in pressure loss and the VAV damper pressure drop increases. Also, the P control offset increases so that the VAV damper pressure drop curves for P and PI control diverge, with the P control curve being at the higher pressure. The lower the flow rate, the greater the P offset and the greater the divergence.

Because horsepower varies as the cube of the air flow rate change the horsepower curves for reduced flow rate will be as shown in FIG. 2-22. This

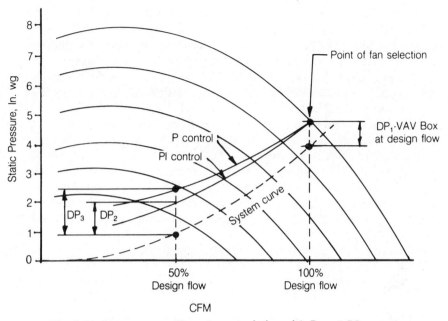

Fig. 2-21. Fan pressure/flow characteristics with P and PI control.

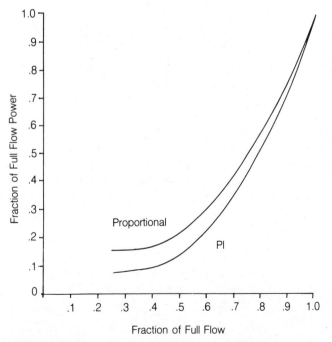

Fig. 2-22. Fan power consumption with P and PI control.

figure shows the fraction of full power versus the fraction of full flow rate, for both P and PI control. While the difference is small at points near full flow it is large at low flow. At 40 percent of full flow rate, the PI horsepower might be as little as half the P horsepower. If we remember that most VAV systems operate most of the time in the range of 50 to 70 percent of design air flow rate, we can see that the difference in energy consumption between P and PI controls can be significant.

Calculating a real value in a specific application is time consuming but not difficult. You simply apply the principles discussed above to a real system with known air flow rates, pressure drops, fan performance, and VAV damper performance. If load variations are calculated, by computer or bin methods, the operating hours at each fraction of design air flow rate can be calculated and applied to a fan horsepower curve as in FIG. 2-22. When the result is integrated (hours times horsepower) the energy quantities and resulting costs can readily be estimated.

Someone ought to write a computer program!

References

1. R.W. Haines, "Supply Fan Volume Control in a VAV System," in part 3 of this book.

2. _____, "Control Valve Selection," in part 4 of this book.

Reset schedules*

One of the basic ideas in any control system design for energy conservation is reset of temperature controller setpoints. And reset, unquestionably, does save energy. The questions to be answered are:

1. What points should be reset?
2. How much reset should be used?
3. What variable should control the reset?
4. How can the reset requirements best be presented to the controls contractor?

Points to be reset

Room temperature control points are usually reset in what is called a *setback* mode: a lower (or higher) setpoint is used for unoccupied times. Or a setpoint might be reset when changing from heating to cooling (if deadband

---

*September 1985.

control is not used). These are two-position functions relating to two different operating modes and are, therefore, easy to specify.

Reset of mixed air low limit temperature, as part of an economy cycle control system, can be a very effective means of energy conservation. Lowering this setpoint decreases mechanical cooling requirements but might increase heating requirements. It follows that the highest mixed air temperature compatible with the cooling load will require the least heating and therefore conserve the most energy.

Reset of supply air temperature is a common and useful practice. A varying supply air temperature is the basis of design in single-zone, constant-volume systems. In multizone or dual-duct systems, minimizing hot deck temperatures and maximizing cold deck temperatures leads to the least reheating effect and therefore minimizes energy consumption. Varying the supply air temperature in a VAV system seems somewhat contradictory, but it does lead to better ventilation rates and distribution patterns. And, in this case, the energy conservation can be obtained in the chiller plant, by raising the chilled water temperature as the supply air temperature is raised.

How much reset?

Mixed air and supply air temperatures are analog variables. An analog variable can take on any value within the range of the device. The range over which a setpoint should be reset is limited by a very practical question: what should the temperature be to satisfy the heating or cooling load at a given design condition? To answer this question, consideration of the loads and air volumes for at least two and preferably three design conditions is required. A typical range for mixed air is 55 to 65 degrees F. This same range might be appropriate for the cold deck of a dual-duct or multizone unit or the supply air of a VAV system. The hot deck of the multizone or dual duct unit might be reset as low as 75 or 80 degrees F from the high temperature determined by the design. A factor often overlooked is the temperature rise through the supply fan, typically in the order of 1 degree F for every 2 inches wc (water column) of pressure rise across the fan. Thus, the multizone cold deck or VAV supply should always be a few degrees above the mixed air setpoint. For the single-zone unit, the supply air temperature might vary from the maximum required for heating to the minimum required for cooling—a wide range.

What controls the reset?

The most popular method of controlling reset in multizone or dual-duct systems is the discriminator. This device is connected to the temperature sensors in a number of key zones and selects the highest or lowest signal from the several zones. The signal is used for reset of mixed air and hot and cold deck controllers. In theory this is an excellent method. In practice there are problems: an inaccurate sensor might drive the system improperly; a zone that is controlled at a higher or lower setpoint than others might drive the system; the discriminator might not work properly. With a DDC, these problems can be overcome by means of a little extra sophisticated programming. An alternative method is to measure the air volume flow rate and assume that this varies, in a linear way, with load. This applies to hot and cold decks in multizone and dual-duct systems and to VAV systems. The practical difficulty lies in obtaining accurate measurements of air volume. To do this properly requires some fairly expensive industrial quality equipment. With good data, this is a reasonable reset procedure.

The oldest method (still in use) is reset as a function of outdoor air temperature. This is a simple process and reasonably accurate in small buildings with large ratios of exterior exposure compared to floor area. However, the typical high-rise office building has net heating and cooling loads that relate more to internal conditions — people, lights, computer terminals, and the like. Thus, reset from outdoor temperature might not be as energy conserving or satisfactory as one of the other methods.

Defining the reset schedule

There are two methods of presenting the reset schedule to the contractor. The older method is the tabular (FIG. 2-23). The table usually provides high and low end points, thus defining a reset ratio. The newer method is to show the same data graphically (FIG. 2-24). Reset might continue beyond the defined limits, as indicated by the dashed lines. This effect might not be desired; it is then necessary to indicate or define limits beyond which no reset is to take place. The graphical method also allows more complex reset patterns to be presented. An example is a single-zone system in which supply air temperature is reset by return air or room temperature, FIG. 2-25. For this example a 2 degrees F temperature rise through the fan has been assumed.

Reset is important not only for energy conservation but for improving system operation. Any reset procedure should be carefully considered and clearly defined.

Reset Schedule 1	
Outdoor air temperature, °F	Mixed air setpoint, °F
30	65
100	55

Fig. 2-23. Tabular reset schedule.

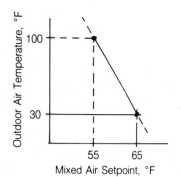

Fig. 2-24. Graphical reset schedule.

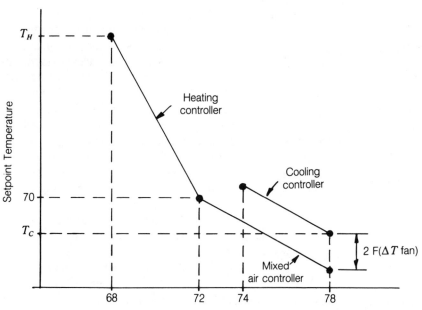

T_H = Design supply air temp. for heating
T_C = Design supply air temp. for cooling

Fig. 2-25. Complex reset schedule.

Intelligent controls*

Artificial intelligence is a buzz word in the computer world. A great deal of research is going on in all areas of computer use — which is just about anything and anywhere these days. Computer chess playing programs are the most conspicuous examples. The more advanced programs are now playing at the grandmaster level.

In the HVAC control world, the present emphasis is on *adaptive* and *self-tuning* control systems. These require a computer but, in many cases, a DDC computer is adequate. In particular, self-tuning systems are for use in DDC because tuning is an operation which applies to the local control loop.

Adaptive control, like any form of artificial intelligence, refers to a computer program or set of programs that provides for analysis and problem solving at a level beyond the simple logical algorithm. Such a program uses empirical and judgmental information obtained from experts in a particular area to develop a set of inference data that can be applied to the problem to come up with answers that might be obtained by the expert. The answers, when applied to solve the problem, provide results that might or might not be optimum, and this information becomes part of the inference data for future problems. The systems are sometimes called *expert systems*. The computer also needs a detailed knowledge base on which to apply the inference data.

Self-tuning controllers are a simple form of adaptive control. Some programs for self tuning are now available, but much needs to be done to perfect the techniques. The principles are straightforward, and they can be discussed here.

The process of tuning a controller requires adjusting the gain to suit the operating conditions. In this book controller gains and system gains are discussed. Because both these gains affect system performance, they must both be taken into account. The only way to do this is to adjust the gain with the system in operation. Present practice is to do this manually, either with a screwdriver for pneumatic and electronic controllers or by adjusting numbers in software for a direct digital controller. In either case, a degree of empirical skill is required, and the process can be difficult. There is an additional problem due to the change in system gain with load. Because this change is nonlinear, the controller gain that is right at one load condition will not be right at another load condition. Thus, the gain finally selected must be a compromise to allow the control loop to be stable under all load conditions.

For a step change in setpoint or load, the typical response with a proportional-only controller is the oscillating wave form shown in FIG. 2-26. This is seldom ideal, and if the gain is low enough for stability, response might be somewhat slow — *sluggish* is the term commonly used. If integral control is added, the response can be more rapid (if the integral gain is properly selected) and can satisfy the quarter-amplitude delay criterion used for accurate tuning

---

*September 1986.

(FIG. 2-27). Another type of response is the critically damped response (FIG. 2-28), which eliminates overshoot at the expense of a somewhat longer response time. Each of these methods will require different gain constants.

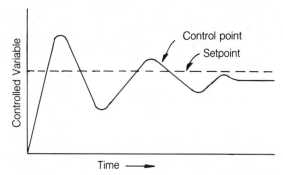

Fig. 2-26. *Oscillating response — proportional control.*

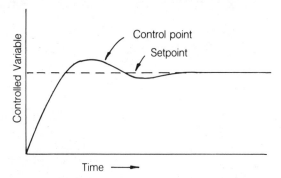

Fig. 2-27. *Quarter amplitude decay response — PI control.*

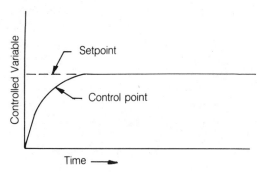

Fig. 2-28. *Critically damped response (PI).*

The self-tuning DDC includes software that enables the controller to adjust the gain in accordance with programmed criteria, eliminating the need for manual tuning. Once the gain constants are established, they are automatically installed in the control algorithm. The gain is still a compromise and will not be ideal under all operating conditions.

Adaptive control, when used for control loop tuning, also includes the software to adjust the gain to the operating conditions. But now the process is continuous; as operating conditions changed the gains are changed accordingly. Some additional software is required to prevent overadjustment during periods when the control system is out of range because of unusual loads or lack of HVAC system capacity.

The use of adaptive control in energy management systems is the subject of considerable research. The possibilities here are great, but little is available in the way of equipment and software. The whole area is one in which you can expect much to happen over the next few years.

*   *   *

Developments have not been as rapid as I hoped when this column was written. I'm still quite sure that adaptive control and intelligent control will become generally available during the 1990s decade, along with many other good things in HVAC control.

Selecting a ΔT for an AHU (air-handling unit)*

The selection of a cooling ΔT for an (AHU) air-handling unit is at once routine, casual and critical. This section discusses the implications of ΔT selection; especially its effect on performance and controllability.

For this analysis, use the psychrometric chart, because this allows a graphical study of the processes. To simplify the analysis, the effects of heat pickup in return air and fan work will be neglected.

For comfort cooling, FIG. 2-29, assume a single zone AHU, an inside (room) design condition of 75 degrees F and 50 percent relative humidity, an outside design condition of 95 degrees F dry bulb and 75 degrees F wet bulb, and 20 percent minimum outside air. Assume also a sensible cooling load of 50,000 Btuh and a latent load of 10,000 Btuh. Then, from the chart, the mixed air condition will be 79 degrees F dry bulb and 65.3 degrees F wet bulb with an enthalpy (h) of 30.2 Btu per pound of dry air. The room condition will include an h of 28.1 and a specific humidity (w) of 0.0092 pounds moisture per pound of dry air.

The design condition of the air supplied to the room is determined in one of two ways:

1. If the psychrometric chart includes a protractor, for example, the ASHRAE chart, a line can be drawn through the room state point with a slope equal to the sensible/total (S/T) ratio (in this case 5/6 or

---

*November 1986.

0.833). In FIG. 2-29, this is line R – S. Theoretically the supply air point can be anywhere on this line. In practice, there are limitations as discussed below.

2. On any chart, the slope of the supply air process line can be calculated by assuming a ΔT and calculating the resulting delta w. In this example a ΔT of 20 degrees F has been used, so that the supply point, S, is at 55 degrees F. Then the design flow will be:

$$50,000 \text{ Btuh}/20°F \times 1.08) = 2315 \text{ cfm} \qquad (2\text{-}4)$$

where: 1.08 = the air factor for standard air

Using this flow, you can calculate the value of Δw:

$$10,000 \text{ Btuh}/(2315) \text{ cfm} \times 60 \times 0.075 \times 1059) = 0.0009 \ (\Delta w) \ (2\text{-}5)$$

where: 60 = minutes per hour
     0.075 = standard air density, pounds per cubic feet
     1059 = latent heat of vaporization at 60°F, Btu per lb

The Δw of 0.0009 subtracted from the room w of 0.0092 equals 0.0083, the needed w of the supply air at point S. Then, from the chart, the supply air properties are 55 degrees F dry bulb, 53.3 degrees F wet bulb, $h = 22.2$, $w = 0.0083$ and relative humidity = 90 percent. By projection, the ADP (apparatus dew point) is 51 degrees F.

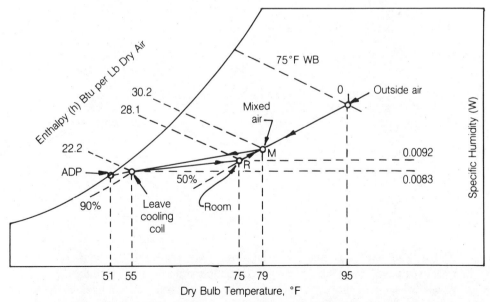

Fig. 2-29. Psychrometric chart for comfort cooling — chilled water.

The figure of 90 percent relative humidity presents a problem because it implies a coil bypass factor of about 14 percent. (See reference 1 at the end of this section.) A present-day cooling coil, even at four rows deep, will do much better, perhaps as good as five percent. It follows that the design condition will not be obtained in practice and, if you try to control the supply air temperature at 55 degrees F, the resulting room condition will be at a somewhat higher humidity than design. In this example the error is probably not serious but the design is, in fact, flawed. While the 20 degrees F ΔT is not too far off, a ΔT of 15 or 16 degrees F would be unrealistic (unless reheat was used — a no-no in these energy-conscious days).

The ADP of 51 degrees F is suitable with supply water at about 45 degrees F. With a DX coil the ADP will tend to be between 40 and 45 degrees F, FIG. 2-30, which will pull the room humidity downward, increasing the load due to dehumidification of outside air. It will also lower the supply air temperature so that the ΔT will be 25 degrees F or more. Then the air flow rate should be changed to 1850 cubic feet per minute. From experience, expect this to result in cold drafts and rapid, two-position response with a tendency to short cycle unless a wide differential is used, with resulting discomfort. The control system will get the blame but actually there is a design deficiency.

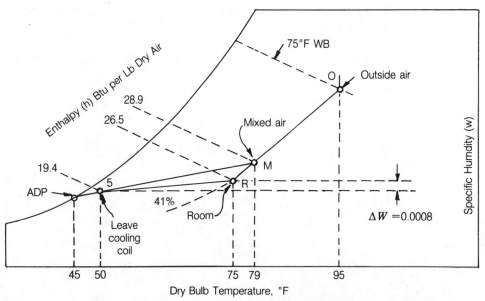

Fig. 2-30. Psychrometric chart for comfort cooling — direct expansion.

At part-load conditions, which prevail most of the time, the DX system will cycle even more often since the supply air temperature does not modulate but varies between design condition when the compressor is running and return air condition when the compressor is off. With chilled water, the throttling of water flow by the control valve allows the bypass factor to increase and the supply air temperature to modulate. Better control can be obtained at the expense of a slight increase in room humidity.

With VAV, accurate control becomes more difficult because of system gains. (See reference 2 at the end of this section.) There is a limited tendency for the entire process to move upward on the psychrometric chart with a resulting increase in room humidity. This will be more noticeable if the supply air temperature is reset upward with decreasing volume as often recommended.

There is a tendency among designers to accept the standard flow of a packaged AHU and to use whatever ΔT results. This can be unrealistic in terms of the flow and coil bypass factor and almost always will result in poor control and wide temperature swings. Packaged unit flows are always adjustable and should be selected at an appropriate value.

This mistake is even easier to make when remodeling and rearranging zones with existing AHUs. "The cfms (flow) are there, why not use them?" philosophy can be hazardous to your comfort.

Only comfort cooling is discussed here. It should be apparent that these phenomena become even more important in systems for process cooling, especially those requiring close control of both temperature and humidity. Then reheat becomes a necessity, but the need for energy conservation requires that you look carefully at the coil ΔT.

References

1. R.W. Haines, "Control of Cooling/ Dehumidifying Coils," in this section of the book.

2. ——, "System Gains," in this section of the book.

* * *

This column brought about the following exchange of correspondence to clear up some ideas that I did not make clear in the initial dissertation. I always appreciated letters like this; they show me that my explanations weren't always as clear and complete as I thought.

A reader writes

"I always read Roger Haines's columns with interest, and November's was no exception. I did have a few questions, however, and would greatly appreciate some clarification.

"1. After presenting an example, Mr. Haines concludes: 'In this example . . . the design is, in fact flawed. While the 20 degrees F ΔT is not too far off, a ΔT of 15 or 16 degrees F would be unrealistic . . .'

"Why is the design flawed? If 20 degrees F ΔT is flawed and 15 degrees ΔT is unrealistic, what is the correct ΔT?

"2. The author continues: 'With a DX coil the ADP will tend to be between 40 and 45 degrees . . . It will also lower the supply temperature so that the ΔT will be 25 degrees F or more. Then the air flow rate should be changed to 1850 cubic feet per minute."

"The designer selects a fan to deliver the chosen air flow based on the ΔT (say 20 degrees F). Why, then, should the air flow be 1850 cubic feet per minute (lower than the design of 2315 cubic feet per minute)? What does the engineer have control over, ΔT or flow?

"I do have a specific case in mind. The space is an exhibition hall with 255 people and almost no heat gain from outside. The conditions are as follows:

Room design: 75°F, 50 percent relative humidity
Outside design: 92 F dry bulb, 74°F wet bulb
Room sensible heat: 125,045 Btuh
Room latent heat: 82,875 Btuh
Outside air sensible heat: 27,475 Btuh
Outside air latent heat: 34,820 Btuh
Fan heat: 15,500 Btuh
Total sensible heat: 168,020 Btuh
Total latent heat: 117,695 Btuh
Grand total heat: 285,700 Btuh

"We selected a 20 degrees F ΔT (SAT = 55 degrees F) and an air flow rate of 5800 cubic feet per minute. Restricted to a DX system we obtained the following computer selection:

Rows/fin: 6/14
Air flow: 5800 cubic feet per minute
Capacity: 291,123 Btuh
Sensible capacity: 195,727 Btuh
Entering dry bulb: 79.7°F
Entering wet bulb: 66.2°F
Leaving dry bulb: 49.02°F
Leaving wet bulb: 48.88°F

"This leaving air temperature of 49 degrees F is less than our selection of 55 degrees F.

"What will the system do? Will the SAT be 49.02 degrees F with a resulting room temperature of 69.02? Or will the SAT be 55 degrees F with a resulting room temperature of 75 degrees F? What will the room relative humidity be? Will we be better off using a packaged system with an air quantity of 10,000 cubic feet per minute?

"Considering that all ducts are exposed, should we insulate them to prevent condensation due to room relative humidity of 65 to 70 percent?

"3. In applications with high latent loads (exhibition halls, community rooms, churches, and swimming pool areas — all with sensible heat ratios of 0.60 or less) and cooling loads of 15 tons and up:

"Do we go with a packaged unit and get a ∆T of approximately 10 to 12 degrees F or do we go with a DX (split system) with about 50 percent fewer cfm (although at a higher initial cost) and ∆T of 20 to 25 degrees F?

"Do we use reheat? Does a bypass damper reduce relative humidity?

"Will ducts sweat with the higher room humidities and lower air flow rates?

"Nowhere but in Roger Haines's column have I found a practical discussion relating theory and what a system actually does. I will greatly appreciate any clarification to the above questions."

Roger Haines replies

Apparently I did not communicate as clearly as I had hoped in my column (it's all very clear to me!). I appreciate the questions and hope I can clear up the problems.

1. In my example with the water coil I showed a 20 degrees F ∆T with a 55 degrees F coil leaving temperature and an ADP of 51 degrees F. A real coil selection would probably have a 52 to 53 degrees F coil leaving temperature; this would follow from a realistic bypass factor of 5 to 7 percent. The resulting 22 to 23 F ∆T would give us 10 to 14 percent extra capacity, which the control system could probably handle. If we had designed for a 15 degree F ∆T, the resulting overcapacity would be over 30 percent. This large system gain would make it difficult for the control system to compensate.

2. The air flow rate and ∆T are dependent variables. The designer can select either one and calculate the other, but the resulting values must be realistic, as discussed above. The specific case cited by the reader, with a DX coil selection at a leaving air temperature of 49.02 degrees F dry bulb and 48.88 degrees F wet bulb, when he wanted 55 degrees F dry bulb, makes my point. This indicates a bypass factor of only 1 or 2 percent. Since it is 6 degrees F lower than the desired 55 degrees F, it would require a significant change in the flow.

Analyzing his specific case, I must first find from the psychrometric chart the feasibility of a room condition of 75 degrees F and 50 percent relative humidity with a sensible/total ratio of 0.60 (determined from the room Btuh values given). If this is plotted on the

ASHRAE chart, using a protractor, FIG. 2-31, the resulting condition line has no ADP and therefore is not possible. It is possible to accomplish the desired result by using reheat, or we can raise the design room relative humidity to about 60 percent, as indicated on the figure. By using reheat, you can control the ΔT to any desired value, but the airflow rate must be increased accordingly and considerable extra energy will be used.

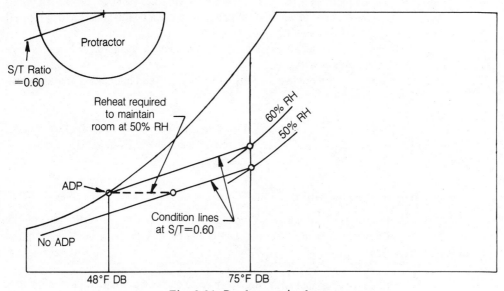

Fig. 2-31. Psychrometric chart.

From his numbers, I infer an outside air quantity of 1470 cubic feet per minute, or 25 percent. This is about 5 cubic feet per minute per person, which is minimal if no smoking is allowed. The new ASHRAE standard on ventilation requires about 15 cubic feet per minute per person. He says this results in a mixed air condition of 79.7 degrees F dry bulb and 62.2 degrees F wet bulb, which he used as the coil entering condition. The fan work will result in a 2.4 degree F rise through the fan [15,500/(5800 × 1.08]. If the fan is in the blow-through position this will raise the coil entering temperature to 82.1 degrees F dry bulb and 66.5 degrees F wet bulb. If, instead, the fan is in the draw-through position, this will raise the temperature of the supply air leaving the fan 2.4 degrees F above the coil leaving temperature, which helps to reduce the ΔT.

To answer the questions about the specific case:

a. The SAT will be 49 degrees F with the fan in blow-through position or 51.4 degrees F with the fan in draw-through position. It will not be 55 degrees F. The extra coil capacity will act as a system gain, encouraging control instability.

b. The room relative humidity will be about 60 percent, as noted.

c. If a packaged system with 10,000 cubic feet per minute air quantity is used it will be necessary to use reheat; a lower relative humidity will be obtained at an increase in operating cost. One possible solution would be to use an internal heat reclaim system. This would add to first cost but would provide most or all of the needed reheat.

d. When the ducts are exposed and supply air temperatures are below the room dew point, as in this case, the ducts must be insulated. Internal insulation could be used.

3. To answer the general questions regarding applications with low sensible/total ratios:

a. The type and size of system and possible ΔT have been discussed above. With a DX coil the ΔT will be in the order of 25 degrees F, which I consider too high. It creates uncomfortably cold, drafty conditions. A ΔT of 10 to 20 degrees F can be obtained by means of reheat. This is limited by most energy codes unless reclaimed heat is used.

b. A bypass damper can be used with a DX coil. The amount of bypass must be limited to prevent icing. Any bypass will tend to increase room humidity since the bypassed air is at a relatively high humidity.

c. Condensation will occur on exposed, uninsulated ducts whenever the ambient dew point exceeds the air temperature with the duct.

Part 3

Systems and Subsystems

The sections in this part of the book are, for the most part, based on real situations that seem interesting enough to be shared. So far as possible, the theory behind each example is emphasized, so that the application to other situations will be possible. But there is no particular sequence, nor any attempt to cover all possible applications. You will probably find a considerable amount of theory and philosophy here.

Control for low humidity*

Control of space humidity, as well as temperature, has always been a fundamental capability of air conditioning. Hospitals and computer rooms, for example, require relative humidities in the 50 to 55 percent range, which are easy to obtain. Some solid-state electronic manufacturing processes require relative humidities of 35 percent or even lower. This is not so easy, and the reheating required is a significant energy consumer. Take a look at the system and controls required to obtain a low humidity environment.

Figure 3-1 is a flow diagram of the traditional HVAC system used to obtain low relative humidities and FIG. 3-2 is a psychrometric chart of the process. Return air from the space, at 75 degrees F and 35 percent relative humidity for example, is mixed with outside air, which in this case is assumed to be at 95 degrees F dry bulb and 78 degrees F wet bulb. The electronic chip manufacturing process requires a great deal of exhaust and makeup air, so the mixture is assumed to be 40 percent outside air. To obtain the specified rh the mixed air must be cooled to a dew point of about 45 degrees F, as can be seen from the psychrometric chart. This requires an ADP (apparatus dew point) of about 44 degrees F and chilled water at 36 to 38 degrees F. For this low temperature, a brine system is frequently used to avoid freezing, with all that implies in reduced heat transfer rates, lower chiller efficiencies and derating of chiller capacity. A 30 degrees F temperature difference between supply air and space temperature (ΔT) is impractical because it results in low air flow rates and wide temperature variations in the space. Because most electronic manufacturing processes require clean-room conditions with high air flow rates, the ΔT is usually 15 degrees F or less. Thus, reheating through 14 to 15 degrees F is needed. For every Btu of reheat, an equal Btu of extra cooling must be supplied.

The efficiency of the system can be improved slightly by using two cooling coils in series, with ordinary chilled water in the first to limit the load on the

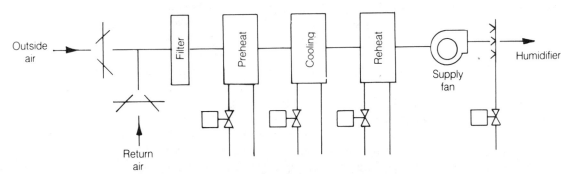

Fig. 3-1. Traditional A/C (air conditioning) system for low relative humidity.

*August 1980.

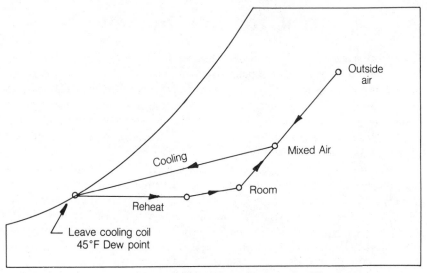

Fig. 3-2. Psychrometric chart for Fig. 3-1.

less efficient brine chiller and coil. Nevertheless, the energy drain due to reheating is still present.

Because the reheating requirement cannot be eliminated, try to make it work for us. Figure 3-3 shows the traditional system with runaround coils added. Part or all of the reheating requirement is now satisfied by using heat extracted in precooling the mixed air. Figure 3-4 is a psychrometric chart showing the process at the same design conditions as in FIG. 3-1. A simple calculation will show that if 14 degrees F of reheat is provided, with an equal amount of precooling, over 30,000 Btuh can be saved for each 1000 cubic feet per minute, as compared with the system of FIG. 3-1.

An interesting result of the runaround system is the lowering of the high limit changeover temperature in the economy cycle control. The reason for this is that cooling of the mixed air is needed to provide the energy for reheat. If the cycle is analyzed on the psychrometric chart at various outside temperatures it can be shown that the changeover high limit is only 1 to 2 degrees F above the mixed air low limit, as shown in FIG. 3-5. Here an outside air condition of 60 degrees F and 80 percent relative humidity is assumed. With the normal high limit changeover 70 to 75 degrees F, the system would use 100 percent outside air. But with a 56 degrees F high limit, the system is on minimum outside air and the mixed air is somewhere in the range of 68 to 70 degrees F. Because the reheat energy comes only from precooling, it is obvious that 70 degrees F mixed air is preferable to 60 degrees F.

Figure 3-6 shows the controls for the runaround system. Mixed air is controlled on an economy cycle, with a 55 degrees F low limit, 56 degrees F high limit, and 40 percent minimum outside air. Preheat is controlled at 50 degrees F and will be used a great deal in the winter in colder climates. Runaround precooling is controlled indirectly, as a function of reheat. The chilled water and brine cooling coils are controlled in sequence to provide air at

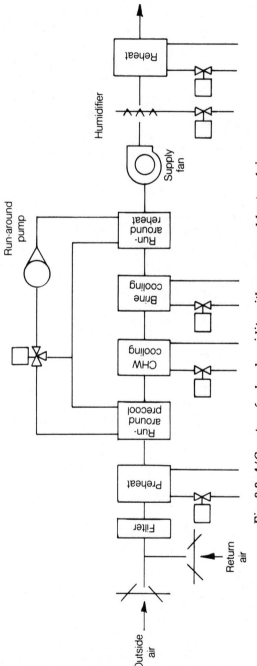

Fig. 3-3. A/C system for low humidity with runaround heat reclaim.

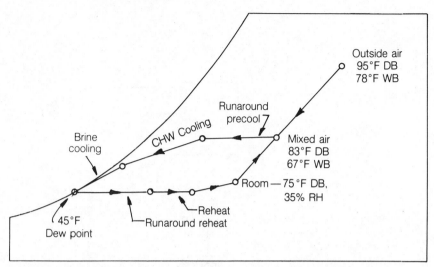

Fig. 3-4. Runaround A/C system for low humidity—summer outside design conditions.

the 45 degrees F dew point, which is the condition required to maintain 35 percent relative humidity at 75 degrees F in the space. The runaround system is controlled by a supply air thermostat which is reset by space temperature. A conventional reheat coil is provided in case the runaround reheat is inadequate.

If the system had more than one zone, each zone would be provided with a conventional reheat coil. The maximum temperature in the zones could be used to reset the supply air thermostat controlling the runaround reheat.

This system will provide space conditions of low humidity with a minimum use of energy as compared with other systems. Chemical dehumidification also can be used.

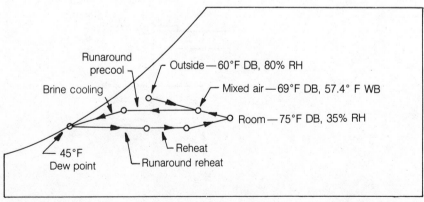

Fig. 3-5. Runaround A/C system for low humidity—intermediate outside conditions.

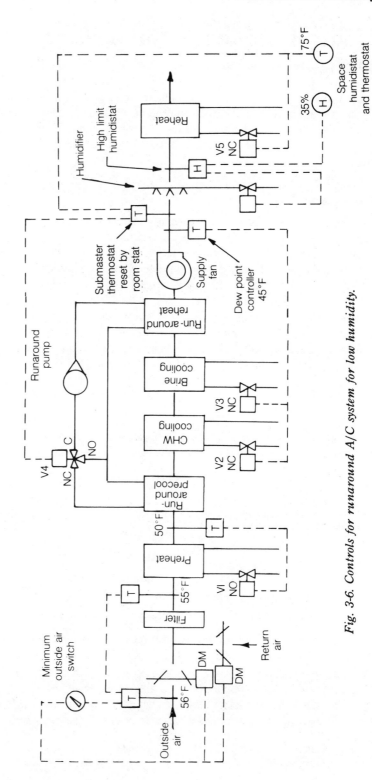

Fig. 3-6. Controls for runaround A/C system for low humidity.

Control sequence for heating*

A reader asks

"What would be the proper control sequence during the heating season for a simple system in which a packaged rooftop heat pump (air-to-air), set at 15 percent continuous ventilation, serves as the main heating plant? Supplementary heating consists of electric baseboard heaters located at the perimeter."

Roger Haines replies

This seems a simple question, regarding a simple HVAC system and deserving a simple answer. But if by proper control the reader means a control system that is energy efficient and still provides comfort, you need to discover alternatives. To do that, you need to look not only at the HVAC system and its controls but also at the building and how it is used.

This type of system might well be used in a small office building so, for discussion purposes, let us assume a one story office building, 40 by 75 feet, with the long axis oriented east-west. The loads might be similar to those in TABLE 3-1 if you assume: the building is constructed with double glass and well-insulated walls and roof; 3 watts per square foot for lights, office machinery, and coffeemakers; one person per 100 square feet; outside design conditions of 95 degrees F dry bulb and 78 degrees F wet bulb in summer and 0 degrees F in winter.

Table 3-1. Cooling and Heating Loads, Btuh

	Cooling Loads	Heating Loads
Transmission—walls, roof, and glass	15,500	63,700*
Solar—glass, walls and roof	41,200	
People—sensible plus latent	13,500	
Lights, etc.	30,700	
Totals	100,900	63,700
Outside air, 750 cubic feet per minute	38,500	56,700
Totals	139,400	120,400

*Night transmission heating load at 55°F inside is 50,000 Btuh

The cooling load would require a 12.5 ton unit with a nominal 5000 cubic feet per minute; 15 percent of this is 750 cubic feet per minute.

The heating load shown in TABLE 3-1 is the gross load. The actual heating requirement at any outside temperature is the gross load less the heat gains due to people, lights and solar. This is shown graphically in FIG. 3-7. Here we can see all the load components as a function of outside air temperature.

*October 1980.

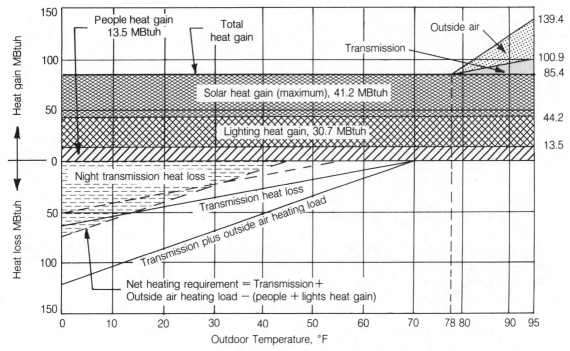

Fig. 3-7. Heating and cooling loads.

Heat gains due to lights and people are essentially constant so long as the building is occupied. Solar gains depend on the amount of cloud and the time of day, so they are not constant. The figure shows the design solar load.

After subtracting heat gains due to lights and people you can see that the net heating requirement becomes zero at 44 degrees F outside for this case. If the solar load is effective the net heating requirement becomes zero at approximately 21 degrees F outside.

If you plot the net heating requirement against the heating capacity of a 12.5 ton heat pump we get FIG. 3-8. The shaded area represents the auxiliary heating requirement. Note the line indicating the night heating requirement at 55 degrees F inside and with no outside air. Auxiliary heat is required only below approximately 21 degrees F outside.

The heat pump with 25 kilowatts of auxiliary heat would provide adequate heat for the building. Why use baseboard radiation? The answer is for comfort.

A little arithmetic will show that, even with double glazing, the interior surface temperature of the glass will be approximately 60 degrees F at 40 degrees F outside and 50 degrees F at 10 degrees F outside. This creates a radiant heat loss from the occupant to the cold surface that can be uncomfortable. Baseboard radiation below the glass can offset the cold glass effect and restore comfort. It can also meet the auxiliary heating requirement, if it is properly sized, eliminating the need for an auxiliary heater in the heat pump. It

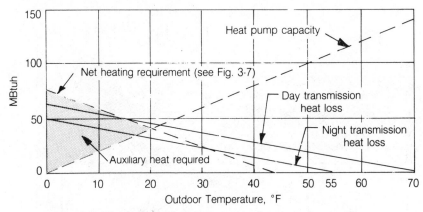

Fig. 3-8. Heating requirements versus heat pump capacity.

can provide the required night heating, allowing the heat pump to be shut down when the building is unoccupied.

From the analysis and data above you can conclude that a good, energy saving system might operate as follows:

1. The heat pump system, without auxiliary heat, should operate only when the building is occupied. This can be accomplished manually or by means of a time clock with manual override.
2. The baseboard radiation should be sized to handle the net heating requirement which, in this case, is greater than the night heating load. The radiation should be allowed to operate below 50 degrees F outside to provide comfort. This radiation can be controlled by means of an outdoor thermostat and relays. As a further refinement the radiation could be zoned by exposure, with a solar compensated outdoor thermostat for each zone. Each space should have a zone radiation thermostat to provide zone control.
3. Night setback should be provided on heating.

The procedure followed above might seem a bit complicated and unjustified for a small system. Actually, the calculations, analysis, figures and writing of this section took less than eight hours. Its not as difficult as it might seem the first time you try it.

Supply- and return-air fan control in a VAV system*

In a VAV system the common method of adjusting supply fan volume is by means of dampers or fan speed controllers. These devices are most often controlled to provide a static pressure in the supply duct main equivalent to the minimum pressure needed in the longest duct run. This is a reasonable and reliable system and gives good results.

Other control methods, some of them rather sophisticated, have been proposed. No matter how it is done, control of the supply fan volume is straightforward and should be basically simple.

But what of the return-relief fan? In a simple system, with a one-to-one relationship between supply and return fans, it is not necessarily adequate to allow the return fan volume to track that of the supply fan. Not all systems have such a one-to-one relationship, particular in retrofit situations. A common arrangement is one with a single-return air fan and two or more supply fans having a common mixed air plenum. Now how should the return fan be controlled?

One of the factors that is often overlooked in VAV system design is the fixed rate of exhaust and design exfiltration. These air quantities should remain constant regardless of the supply air volume. System design normally takes this into account in the minimum outside air setting and the selection of the return air fan at a lower air volume than the supply fan. But system controls often neglect it.

Figure 3-9 shows a VAV system with one supply fan and one return fan. At maximum design conditions the supply fan is delivering 10,000 cubic feet per minute, of which 500 cubic feet per minute is exhausted and 500 cubic feet per minute is allowed to exfiltrate to maintain building pressure. The return fan handles 9,000 cubic feet per minute. At this point the outside air damper should be open to its minimum position of 1,000 cubic feet per minute and the relief damper should be closed. All control systems have the minimum outside air and minimum relief dampers both open — as though the building exhaust did not exist.

For this analysis assume that the relief damper remains closed when the outside air damper is in its minimum position. Then the pressure relationships in the system are as shown by the solid line in FIG. 3-10. The negative pressure in the mixing plenum provides the correct pressure differential across the outside air damper to create a flow of 1,000 cubic feet per minute.

Now, with the outside air damper still in minimum position, assume that the supply fan volume is reduced to 5000 cubic feet per minute (50 percent) and the return fan is controlled to track the supply fan, reducing return volume to 4500 cubic feet per minute (50 percent). From the laws of hydraulics, for 50 percent of flow, the pressure drops through the various parts of the system are

---

*February 1981.

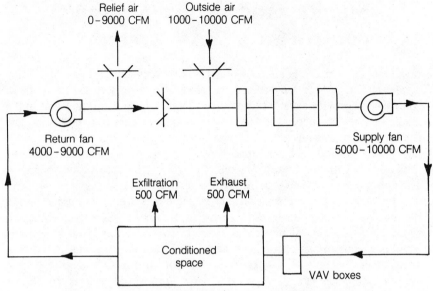

Relief air
0–9000 CFM

Outside air
1000–10000 CFM

Return fan
4000–9000 CFM

Supply fan
5000–10000 CFM

Exfiltration
500 CFM

Exhaust
500 CFM

Conditioned
space

VAV boxes

Fig. 3-9. Variable-air volume system.

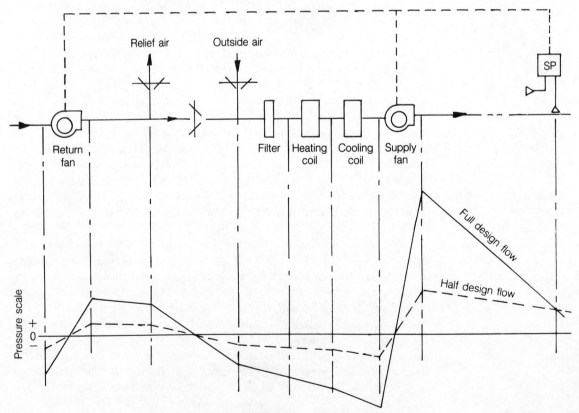

Relief air

Outside air

SP

Return
fan

Filter

Heating
coil

Cooling
coil

Supply
fan

Full design flow

Half design flow

Pressure scale

+

0

−

Fig. 3-10. Pressure profile in a VAV system.

reduced to 25 percent of their initial values. The new pressure curve would look like the broken line in FIG. 3-10. The supply static pressure control requires that its point be at a constant pressure. The pressure in the mixed air plenum will be considerably higher than the pressure at 10,000 cubic feet per minute, resulting in a lower differential pressure across the outside air damper and reducing the outside air flow by 50 percent or even more. This changes the building internal pressure with respect to outside and may even violate code requirements for minimum ventilation air.

There are at least two ways to ensure that the minimum outside air is obtained under all supply fan volume conditions.

Figure 3-11 shows the volume flow sensing method. Air flow sensors are provided in both supply and return ducts. The setpoint of the return fan volume controller, C1, is reset by the supply air flow sensor so that a constant differential is maintained between the two air volumes. The supply air volume is controlled as usual by the duct static pressure.

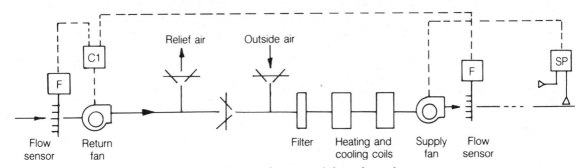

Fig. 3-11. Return fan control from fan volume.

Another method of obtaining minimum outside air is to maintain a constant pressure across the outside air damper by maintaining the mixed air plenum pressure at some negative level with respect to an outdoor reference, as shown in FIG. 3-12. This pressure regulator is used to control the return fan volume. The result is the pressure relationships shown for full and partial air flow.

To simplify the discussion, assume minimum outside air. If economy cycle controls are used, the relationships become very complicated and probably can be analyzed dynamically only by means of a computer. The control system described here does provide minimum outside air under all conditions of operation and does it quite simply.

Note that the system in FIG. 3-11 operates satisfactorily only in a one-to-one relationship between supply and return fans. The system in FIG. 3-12 will control satisfactorily under any complex arrangement of supply and return fans with a common mixing plenum.

*   *   *

This section is only the one element in a lengthy discussion that is still going on. The first point made was that trying to sense static pressure in a

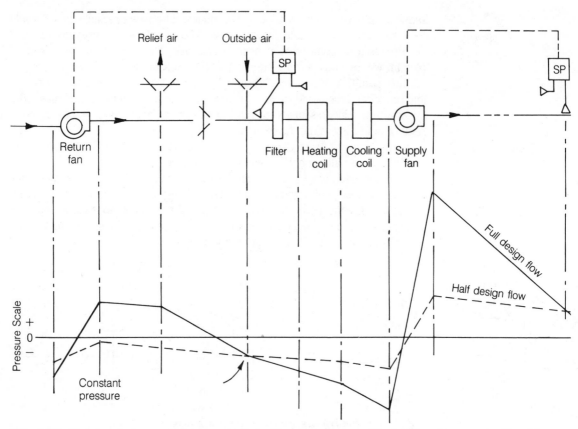

Fig. 3-12. Return air fan control from mixed air plenum pressure with resulting pressure profiles (also see Fig. 3-10).

mixing plenum was an exercise in futility. The typical mixing plenum is very turbulent and in any location the static pressure will not be stable. In the specific case which I designed the sensor was actually located just downstream of the air filter, in a region of stability but one in which the pressure changes gradually as the filters load up. This system worked very well.

The major point of discussion is whether return fans are really needed. Some engineers feel that return fans should never be used — relief, perhaps, but return never. One of the specific problems is the velocity pressure on the return damper, which makes it even more difficult to control properly. My opinion is that return fans should be used only when the return duct system pressure drop exceeds 0.5 inches of water column. Even then, use them with care and select a very low pressure rise across the fan. The matter of maintaining minimum outside air at all times is a related problem but really requires a separate solution. The best approach appears to be that of using a minimum outside air fan to ensure that outside air requirements are met.

Economy cycle controls*

Economy cycle control of outside air, return-air and relief-air dampers is a simple, well-understood procedure — at least, it appears so. There are a few control sequences lately that purport to be economical and good but introduce some complications to the nice, simple system. Here are implications of these sequences.

First, look at the conventional economy cycle control, shown in FIG. 3-13. Controller C1, with sensor T1 in the mixed air, controls the damper operators and, thus, the proportions of outside and return air to maintain a minimum mixed air temperature — usually 55 to 66 degrees F. When the outside air exceeds a switchover point, usually 70 to 75 degrees F, relay R1 switches control of the dampers from C1 to minimum position switch SW1. This is basically simple and independent of the rest of the air conditioning unit controls. Some alternative systems are shown in FIGS. 3-14 through 3-17. These are systems that are actually installed and working.

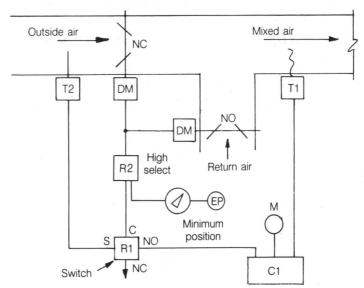

Fig. 3-13. Conventional mixed-air economy cycle control.

The system in FIG. 3-14 includes a single coil which is used for either heating or cooling (two-pipe system) with a manual summer-winter change-over. The manual changeover is also used, through relay R1, to switch the damper control to minimum outside air in summer. In winter the dampers are controlled by the room thermostat, T2, with discharge air temperature sensor T1 acting as a low limit. This is very much like the old-style unit ventilator control. A possibility of coil freeze-up exists if the room becomes too warm, calling for 100 percent outside air when the outside temperature is below

---

*March 1981.

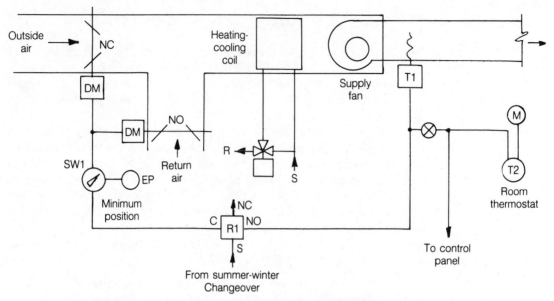

Fig. 3-14. Outside air control from room thermostat with manual changeover.

freezing. The low limit might not prevent freezeup because it has no effect on water flow to the coil. Otherwise, the system works. Note that it is an open-loop system where outside air is concerned and, therefore, is not necessarily economical.

In FIG. 3-15 the logic panel L1, incorporates outside air switchover and minimum outside air damper position. At outside air temperatures below the

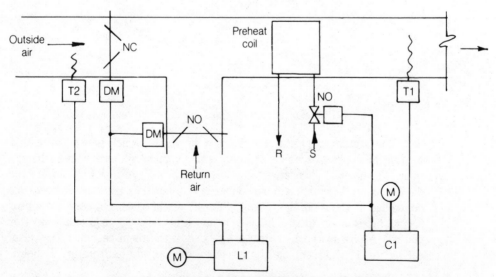

Fig. 3-15. Outside air control from preheat discharge.

switchover point the dampers are controlled by C1, with sensor T2 in the air leaving the preheat coil. C1 also controls the preheat coil valve, so T2 senses not the real mixed air temperature but a preheated mixed air temperature. Again, this is open-loop control so far as the dampers are concerned. When the damper motors and the preheat coil valve are properly sequenced, this system works well under steady-state conditions. However, the possibility of freeze-up exists on morning startup with the coil hot (the normally open valve would provide for this). Sensor T2 would request 100 percent outside air and no preheat water flow. In the system where this was observed, the air conditioning units are operated continuously, so there is no problem.

Figure 3-16 shows a VAV system with cooling only because it serves an interior area. Changeover to minimum outside air is accomplished by a temperature sensor in the chilled water supply. When there is no chilled water the dampers are controlled by a discharge air temperature thermostat. When the coil is not active this thermostat acts as a mixed air controller. It also controls the cooling coil valve.

Figure 3-17, at first glance, looks like a conventional economy cycle control. Minimum outside air is provided by a separate damper, which is open when the supply fan is running. However, the primary power (originally, the main air supply) for controller C1 comes ultimately as a modulated supply from room thermostat T2 (see note at the end of this section). The effect of this is to provide more outside air when the room is warm and less when the room is cool. Sensor T1 in the mixed air acts as a low limit only and cannot cause an increase in the outside air supply unless the room thermostat signal allows it. Changeover from a central enthalpy controller is provided to serve six air conditioning units. The manual switch can be used to open or close the outside air damper but, in the open position, T2 still acts as a low limit.

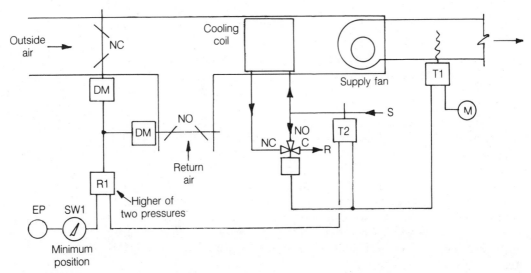

Fig. 3-16. Outside air control from supply air (chilled water used for changeover.

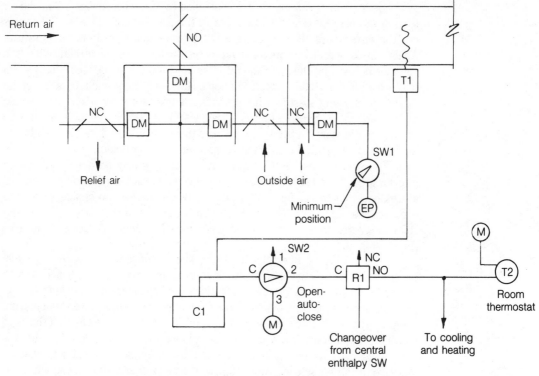

Fig. 3-17. Outside air control from room thermostat.

As noted, all of these systems are installed and working, using pneumatic controls. They were designed and installed by four different control manufacturers. All have some open-loop features. That is, the effect of the control action is not sensed directly by the sensor that initiates the control action. Therefore, it is difficult to analyze what is really happening.

The real question is: "Why complicate a simple control system when the results achieved cannot be shown to be better?"

*　*　*

The system of FIG. 3-17 would not work with most present-day commercial pneumatic controllers. The main air supply must be maintained at all times. Varying the main supply air to these instruments will cause the controller to lose calibration.

Note that both this and the next section do not discuss enthalpy changeover controllers. My experience, and that of my friends in the industry, is that enthalpy controllers are not cost effective and are a high maintenance item. In many cases, the operators simply disconnect them. While I like to maintain an open mind, I'm going to need a lot of convincing to change my mind on this item.

Economy cycle control*

The energy crisis has forced the industry to take a hard look at all favorite HVAC control procedures. Before, the simple question was how to get the best comfort control, with little regard for energy. Now the question is how to obtain comfort but with a minimum expenditure of energy. Some ideas of comfort have been reconsidered. It is not necessary to maintain 75 degrees F in the summer and 72 degrees F in the winter. EBTR (emergency building temperature regulations) might go a bit too far with 65 and 80 degrees F but 70 and 78 degrees F are reasonable.

One of the favorite sacred cows is the economy cycle for control of mixed air. After all, isn't it, by definition, economical? For years mixed air control setpoints of 55 degrees F low limit and about 70 degrees F outside have been used for changeover to minimum outside air. I never questioned this until a few weeks ago.

Recently, our office was using a computer program to compare energy consumption under various control strategies. The base line assumed a fixed outside air volume at all times. Then we ran an economy cycle with 55 degrees F low limit and 70 degrees F changeover. Sure enough, the cooling energy use went down. But the heating energy consumption went up. Drastically!

After I got over the initial shock and said, "This can't be." We sat down and started analyzing the situation.

Most air handling systems are designed to use an 18 to 20 degrees F ΔT; that is, to maintain a 78 degree F room temperature, supply air should be at 58 to 60 degrees F. This is our first fallacy. We have failed to adjust our mixed air temperature to the new space temperature requirements — 78 to 80 degrees F, rather than 75 degrees F.

But this 20 degree F ΔT is needed only at peak cooling loads, which do not occur when the outside air is below 70 degrees F. Now we need perhaps as little as 10 or 12 degrees F ΔT, or a supply air temperature of 66 to 68 degrees F. But our mixed air might be 100 percent outside air at 55 to 60 degrees F. So, it is necessary to preheat this air 8 to 13 degrees F. Thus, the extra heating we had overlooked.

To determine the extent of this preheating, we looked at an average weather profile for Cincinnati. These data show the number of hours per year in each 5 degrees F temperature bracket. As can be seen from TABLE 3-2, almost half the total hours per year are at temperatures between 40 and 70 degrees F. More importantly, if you look only at the 8 AM to 4 PM hours of normal occupancy for office buildings, you find that 40 percent of these, or 1158 hours, are in the 40–70 degree F bracket. A little simple arithmetic will show that preheating 1000 cubic feet per minute of air through an average of 10 degrees F for 1158 hours requires 12,500,000 Btu per year.

At that point we agreed that the 55 degree F fixed minimum is wasteful. So how should we control for minimum use of energy? Simply raising the

---

*April 1981.

Table 3-2. Weather Data for Cincinnati (showing number
of hours annually in temperature brackets by time of day)

Temperature Range °F	Annual hours by time of day			Total Annual Hours
	Midnight to 8 A.M.	8 A.M. to 4 P.M.	4 P.M. to Midnight	
100-104	0	0	0	0
95-99	0	7	1	8
90-94	0	61	17	78
85-89	0	171	70	241
80-84	6	276	152	434
75-79	61	306	253	620
70-74	264	273	329	866
65-69	347	223	285	855
60-64	308	200	251	759
55-59	267	181	209	657
50-54	251	174	200	625
45-49	210	192	200	602
40-44	222	188	214	624
35-39	253	212	218	683
30-34	267	199	227	693
25-29	197	119	130	446
20-24	115	61	79	255
15-19	67	34	39	140
10-14	34	23	22	79
5-9	23	13	11	47
0-4	15	5	6	25
−5/−1	7	1	3	11
−10/−6	2	0	0	2
−15/−11	0	0	0	0
−20/−16	1	0	0	1

minimum is not enough, for the mixed air temperature really should be a function of cooling or heating load in the building.

The schemes that follow are not necessarily the last word on this subject. Ideally, perhaps, we should be using a microprocessor. But the schemes have the advantage of simplicity and, in retrofit situations, require very few additional devices.

Figure 3-18 shows a single-zone system. In this case the room thermostat is used to control everything. Low-limit thermostats are used on both mixed air and supply air. The principal change from conventional systems is the sequencing of valves and dampers.

When the outside temperature is below 70 degrees F and with the room temperature 2 degrees F or more below the room thermostat setpoint, the heating valve is fully open, the cooling valve is closed and the outside air damper is open only to minimum position. As the room temperature increases the heating valve begins to close and is fully closed at slightly below the room

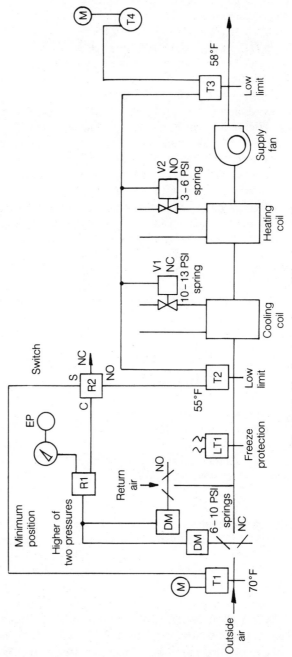

Fig. 3-18. Single-zone air conditioning unit.

thermostat setpoint. As the temperature continues to rise, the dampers begin to modulate to provide more outside air, subject to the 55 degrees F low limit. If the outside air is insufficient to cool the room then, at a room temperature slightly above the room thermostat setpoint, the cooling valve begins to open. This sequence bears a striking resemblance to the old unit ventilator control cycle II (ASHRAE *Handbook*, 1979 Equipment, page 27.3).

A conventional outside air high limit is used to return the outside air to minimum above 70 degrees F outside. Any attempt to improve on this without a microprocessor results in a great deal of complexity.

Either a standard thermostat or a deadband thermostat can be used as the room thermostat. Figure 3-19 shows the concept adapted to VAV. Here, the supply temperature is reset as a function of flow. This reset must be done within some limits, to provide for interior zones. The supply air thermostat then controls the valves and dampers as described above. One of the problems observed in energy studies is the typical overdesign of most systems. It is highly desirable when designing for or converting to VAV to reduce the design air quantity to an absolute minimum to avoid excessive energy expenditure.

Figure 3-20 shows a double-duct system with discriminator control. Because it is not practical to use all zones for the discriminator, it is sufficient to use 6 to 10 selected zones, together with an air-flow sensor. The cold-duct temperature controller is then used to control the preheat coil and mixing dampers in sequence so that preheat is used only when the outside air damper is in the minimum position. The hot-valve discriminator control is typical.

Controls for a multizone system would be identical except that the air flow sensors would be deleted.

Figure 3-21 shows a reheat system. A discriminator control, using 6 to 10 selected zones, controls preheat, cooling coils and mixing dampers in a sequence similar to that of the single zone of FIG. 3-18. Low-limit thermostats are provided in supply air and mixed air.

As stated, these ideas are not necessarily the last world. They are attempts to deal with the part load condition with a minimum of energy use, while still maintaining comfort. And, they are basically simple. These are the tests to use in any control system design.

* * *

These ideas are definitely not the last word. Since writing this, I have become disillusioned with discriminators, which are great in principle but difficult to maintain and subject to erroneous operation when one or more of the inputs is incorrect. I no longer recommend the use of discriminators but, when a computer is being used and the inputs can be tested for validity, then discrimination can be very useful. So the principles in this article are OK but probably won't work well in practice with a mechanical discriminator. Our present philosophy is to reset mixed air and hot deck from outside air and cold deck not at all. The range of allowable reset on a cold deck is small in any case. Also, I often use 75 degrees F outdoor air temperature as the changeover point, since return air temperatures usually exceed 75 degrees F.

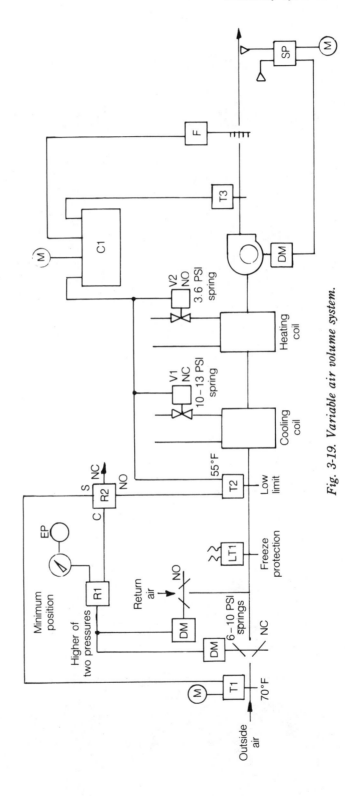

Fig. 3-19. Variable air volume system.

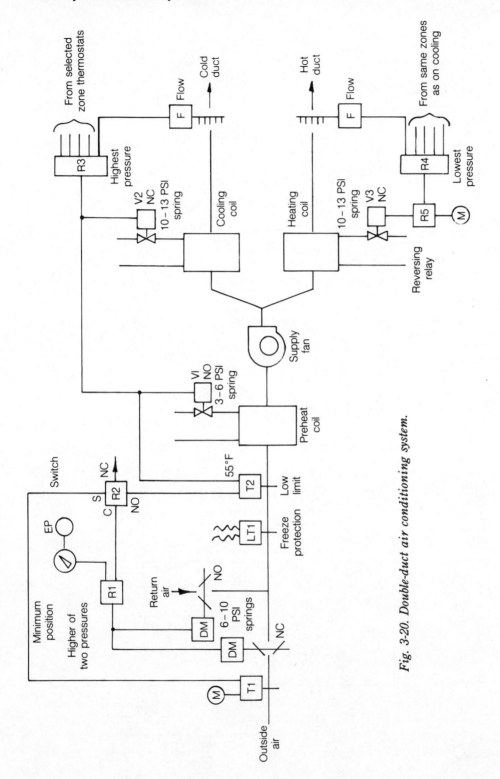

Fig. 3-20. Double-duct air conditioning system.

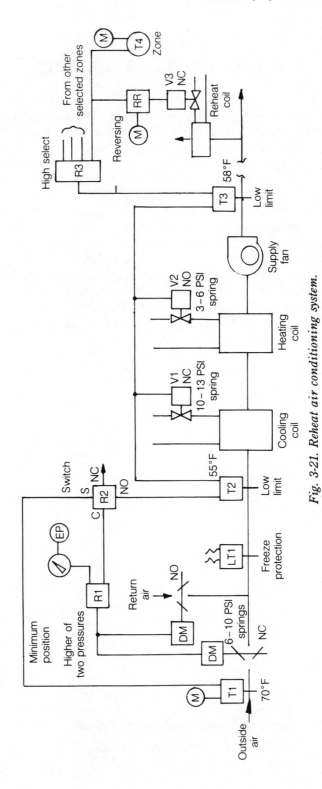

Fig. 3-21. Reheat air conditioning system.

Environmental control in a standards laboratory*

Most of you will never have the opportunity of designing environmental control for a standards laboratory. Still, you never know. This topic can illustrate a very important point. The building, the HVAC system, and the control system are all part of a whole. If any part is deficient, the whole suffers. This is never more evident than in a standards laboratory.

A laboratory for primary or secondary standards is a room in which master gauge blocks are kept. These gauges are used to check the production gauges used in the manufacturing process. Because of the close tolerances involved — sometimes millionths of an inch — close control of temperature and humidity is essential. *Close control* for a secondary standards laboratory means plus or minus one-fifth of a degree F and 3 to 5 percent relative humidity.

In an ordinary room, even when well insulated, the wall, floor and ceiling surface temperatures can be several degrees different from the space air temperature. The air supply temperature can be 15 to 20 degrees F different from that of the space. Obviously, with these conditions we have no chance of maintaining the needed accuracy.

First, as shown in FIG. 3-22, the room must be designed to provide a surface temperature very close to space air temperature. For the walls, this is done by providing a well insulated main wall with a light wall furred out 3 to 4 inches. The space between the walls becomes the return air channel, with

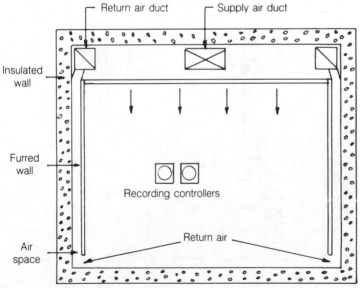

Fig. 3-22. Section through a standards laboratory.

*October 1981.

return air entering at the bottom and leaving at the top. In this way the wall temperature is held at or very near the space temperature. The ceiling is used as a continuous supply grille (perforated ceiling) with supply air from the insulated space above. Thus, the ceiling temperature will be close to the supply air temperature. The floor must be well insulated and, because of return air movement across it, the floor temperature remains close to the space air temperature.

The supply air temperature must always be close to the space temperature because with a large temperature difference the required tolerance could not be maintained. A large volume of air flow is required with, at most, one or two degrees F difference from the design space temperature. Ordinary heating and cooling media temperatures will not be satisfactory because large differences between these media temperatures and the supply air temperature will cause momentary *bumps* (upsets) as control valves are opened even a small amount. Hot water supply temperature for reheat should not exceed 80 degrees F for 70 degrees F room design and secondary pumping must be used to keep a uniform temperature across the face of the coil. Steam is not suitable. Chilled water supply temperature should be as high as possible, while maintaining the needed humidity, and secondary pumping should be used. Direct expansion coils are not suitable. Electric reheat can be used if SCR (silicon controlled rectifier) or similar modulating control is used. The important thing is to maintain a very small differential between supply air and space temperatures. Energy conservation is not really feasible although the amount of cooling required may be controlled as a function of both temperature and humidity to minimize reheat.

Now that you have a room and an air handling system that are suitable for the requirements, it is relatively easy to design a control system, FIG. 3-23. Controls must be of the best industrial quality with electronic sensors and controllers using PI mode. Water valves can be pneumatic with transducers for interface to the electronic controllers. Electronic valve operators can also be used.

Recording controllers are usually provided to show that temperature and humidity criteria are met. With this design of room, HVAC system and control system, it is possible to meet the criteria for a primary or secondary standards lab.

To restate the point made in the opening paragraph: the provision of the best possible control system is not sufficient by itself. The room and the HVAC system must also be suitable. Too often, in buildings with less stringent requirements, this fact is overlooked. It is, however, always true. Always look beyond the controls to the building and the HVAC system in analyzing HVAC control problems.

*　*　*

Related articles that might help in understanding this discussion are: "System Gains," in part 2 of this book, and "Selecting Control Valves," in part 4 of this book.

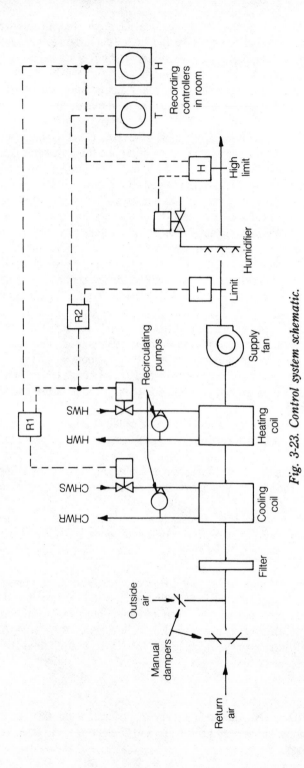

Fig. 3-23. Control system schematic.

Air flow balance in a laboratory*

Research laboratories with fume hoods present some very special problems in the control and balancing of air flow rates, especially if the hoods are not used continually but are turned on and off as needed. The problems to be addressed are these:

1. Makeup (supply) air to the room must equal the exhaust through the hood or hoods. In many cases, makeup should be slightly less than exhaust to create a negative pressure in the lab with respect to adjacent spaces.
2. When the hood is not in use, supply air flow can be reduced to the amount necessary to control the environment. Because this air cannot be returned, it is necessary to provide some general exhaust capability for this mode of operation.
3. Under both operating conditions, the supply air must have the proper temperature and humidity to control the environment.

It should be noted that there might be more than one hood in the room, and most laboratories will have several rooms. In general, air can be returned from offices and corridors but most laboratory air systems use 100 percent outside air. Therefore, it is advisable to provide heat reclaim for energy conservation.

Problem solving

To solve the problems properly with minimum energy expenditure, it appears that variable volume control of both supply and exhaust is needed.

Exhaust air volumes can be controlled by a separate exhaust fan for each hood, and many systems do this. If corrosive or toxic chemicals are used in the hood, a separate exhaust is required. If heat reclaim is used, it is preferable to provide a common exhaust fan with variable volume controls and with dampers at each hood. The same common fan can be used for general exhaust, although balancing becomes difficult because of the relatively high pressure drop through the hoods. To limit total exhaust air flow, the general exhaust should have a damper that closes when the hood is in use.

Supply air flow rates can be controlled in several ways. For energy conservation, it would be best to use outside air without conditioning it. This unconditioned air cannot be introduced into the room generally but must be supplied at or near the hood. Sometimes special hoods are used in which makeup air is supplied through slots at the face of the hood as shown in FIG. 3-24. Enough room air must be used to create sufficient flow from room to hood to prevent any spill of contaminated air. This amounts to at least 50 percent of the total exhaust, which might be more than is needed for environmental control in the room.

---

*November 1981.

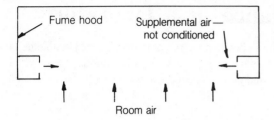

Fig. 3-24. Fume hood with supplemental unconditioned makeup air.

Another method is to introduce the unconditioned air near the hood in the hope that most of it will be exhausted without upsetting the thermal balance of the room. In general this method has not been satisfactory, because spill does occur, and the environment in the working area in front of the hood is often unacceptable.

The best solution from an environmental control standpoint is to provide conditioned makeup air to the room, varying the quantity to match the exhaust. The increased energy consumption can be offset, at least in part, by heat reclaim.

One method of controlling supply air flow to match exhaust is shown in FIG. 3-25. This control system is designed for a room with two hoods and pneumatic controls are shown. The principles can be applied using any type of

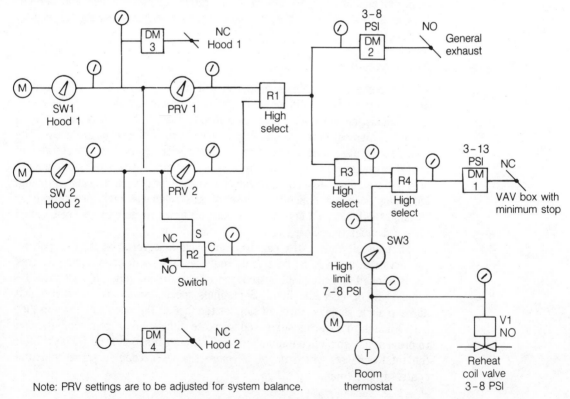

Note: PRV settings are to be adjusted for system balance.

Fig. 3-25. Air flow control with two fume hoods in one laboratory room.

control power, including DDC. The idea could be used for any number of hoods, though the degree of complexity increases exponentially.

Each hood has a damper in the exhaust duct with a manual switch. When the operator wishes to use hood 1, he or she turns switch 1 (SW1) to the open position. Control air flows to the damper motors to open the hood exhaust and close the general exhaust. A preset pressure reducing valve provides control air to open the supply-air VAV damper to a position corresponding to the makeup need for hood 1.

A similar pattern is followed for hood 2. If both hoods are in use, relay R2 is switched to provide 15 pounds per square inch control air to the VAV damper, opening it to full makeup position for two hoods.

If neither hood is in use, the VAV damper is controlled by the room thermostat, which could be a deadband or summer-winter type. This thermostat also controls the room reheat coil, if needed. Note that the room thermostat can open the VAV damper only to a limited extent, as needed for environmental control.

*   *   *

Since this was written, there have been a number of solutions published. Most modern systems use true VAV, with exhaust and makeup air flows controlled to create a pressure gradient from corridor to lab, to hood. Accurate control of these pressure gradients was not possible with the older differential pressure sensors, but is possible using hot-wire anemometers to measure pressure differential as a function of air flow velocity from one pressure level to another. But there is no reason why the system described in this section should not be used for older-style nonmodulating hood exhaust flows.

In the book, *Control Systems for Heating, Ventilating and Air Conditioning*, (Fourth edition) on pages 229 through 232, a large VAV laboratory system with heat reclaim is described. This system uses pressure differential sensors and probably required a great deal of maintenance. At this point, I would use velocity sensors instead of pressure sensors. We continue to learn, I hope.

Supply fan volume control in a VAV system*

A VAV HVAC system consists of an air-handling unit that supplies air at (usually) a fixed temperature through a duct system to a terminal unit at each zone. The terminal unit has a modulating damper and it might also include a reheat coil. Each damper is modulated by a zone thermostat in response to cooling demand in the zone. Air volume to the zone is reduced as cooling load decreases. The philosophy is that a reduction in the air volume will also save fan work energy.

---

*August 1983.

As the individual zone dampers are modulated, the total air supply must vary to match the sum of the requirements for all zones in the system. This means that the supply fan volume will change. The purpose of this section is to discuss the various means of controlling supply fan volume and to evaluate them on the bases of economic and operational criteria.

Typically, actual operating air volumes will vary between 50 and 80 percent of design cfm (flow in cubic feet per minute). See TABLE 3-3. For the purposes of this discussion, a reduction to 70 percent of design flow will be used. In accordance with the fan laws, this means a reduction to 49 percent of the design system pressure and 34 percent of the design fan horsepower. In practice there are complicating factors and these reductions are not obtained.

Table 3-3. Comparison of Fan Volume Control Methods

Method	Comparative First Cost	Comparative Energy Use	Control Quality
No control	None	High	Poor
Discharge damper	Low	High	Good
Inlet vane damper	High	Low	Good
Speed control	High	Lowest	Good

The simplest method of control is no control of the fan volume. As the system volume is reduced the fan simply rides up its curve, as shown in FIG. 3-26. At design flow the system ΔP (pressure drop) and the terminal ΔP

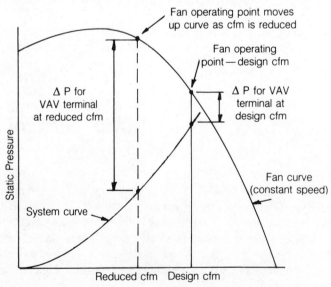

Fig. 3-26. Fan and system curves — no volume control.

combine as shown to determine the fan operating point. As the flow is reduced, the ΔP of the terminal must increase more than it normally would, to compensate for the increased fan pressure and reduced system ΔP. The static pressure in the system can increase by a factor of as much as three or four; ducts have been blown apart under these conditions. The terminal units tend to be noisy because of the high ΔP. Very little fan horsepower is saved since the increase in fan pressure offsets the decrease in flow. This method is not recommended except in special cases.

Fan volume can be controlled by means of dampers or by variation of the fan speed. Control is based on maintenance of a constant SP (static pressure) at some point in the duct system. The recommended location is one-half to two-thirds of the distance between the supply fan and the first terminal. A pressure profile of such a VAV system at design conditions is shown by the solid line of FIG. 3-27. To simplify the discussion the return fan is assumed to be controlled to provide a fixed pressure in the mixed air plenum.

Reference pressure is room pressure. Starting with a negative pressure in the mixed air plenum (to provide for pressure drop across the outside air louver and damper), the static pressure becomes more negative, due to drops across filter and coils, until it enters the fan. Here the pressure is increased to a value sufficient to overcome pressure drops in the duct system and across the terminal units. The point of sensing for constant duct static pressure is indicated.

The simplest damper control method is the use of a discharge damper in the duct (see the dashed line in FIG. 3-27). As indicated in FIG. 3-28, the effect of this is similar to FIG. 3-26 except that now the discharge damper takes care of excess fan pressure, allowing the terminal unit to provide better and quieter control. Duct pressure downstream of the damper does not increase. Fan horsepower is not appreciably reduced. The no-control profile is also shown in FIG. 3-27.

The preferred dampering method is by means of inlet vane dampers at the fan. Figure 3-29 shows the system pressure profile. Figure 3-30 shows the fan operating effects. As the inlet vane damper partially closes it imparts a spin to the air entering the fan and actually changes the fan performance curve (a wrong-way damper creates a reverse spin and degrades the fan performance). The result, if the damper is installed correctly, is a reduction in fan operating pressure with a resultant saving of fan horsepower.

The best method of saving energy is to vary the fan speed by means of a speed changing drive, such as modulating clutch, or by means of a motor speed controller. This provides the greatest energy saving, approaching the theoretical. Less horsepower is required than with any of the other methods. This is illustrated by the dashed line in FIG. 3-29 and the fan curves in FIG. 3-31. Each change of fan speed produces a new fan curve, parallel to the other curves.

Because the ΔP through the terminal unit must increase to decrease the cfm to its zone, the system and fan ΔP do not vary in strict accordance with the fan laws; the horsepower reduction as flow in cubic feet per minute is reduced

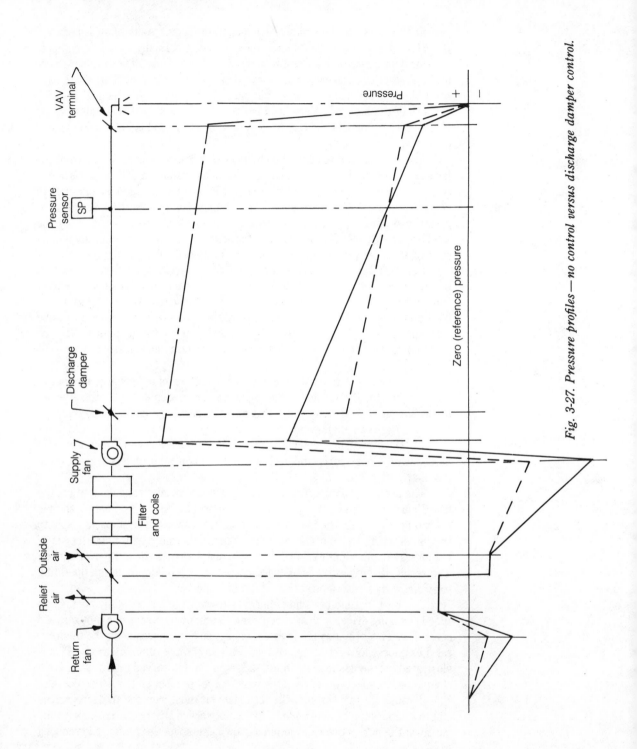

Fig. 3-27. Pressure profiles—no control versus discharge damper control.

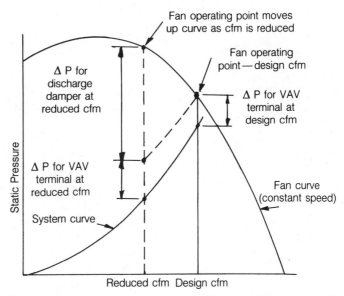

Fig. 3-28. Fan and system curves — discharge damper control.

is not as great as theory would predict. Nevertheless, it is substantial if inlet vane dampers or fan speed controls are used.

This discussion assumes that the control of static pressure at a specified point in the duct system is invariable. This will be true only if PI (proportional-plus-integral) control is used. (See reference 1 at the end of this section.) If simple P (proportional) control is used, there will always be some offset of the control point from the setpoint, as shown by the dashed line in FIG. 3-32. In this case, the pressure at the sensor point will be higher than design and the offset will increase as the flow decreases. This section causes the fan pressure to increase, with a resulting increase in fan horsepower. For this reason, it is recommended that PI control always be used with this system. Retrofit of an existing P control to PI control should have a short-term payback. Also, the use of a high-quality ΔP sensor is recommended.

Reference

1. G. Shavit and S.G. Brandt, "Dynamic Performance of a Discharge Air Temperature System with a PI Controller," *ASHRAE Journal*, September 1982, pages 37 – 41.

*   *   *

There is no magic about the selection of the duct static pressure sensing point. Just remember that the sensed pressure must be sufficient to provide

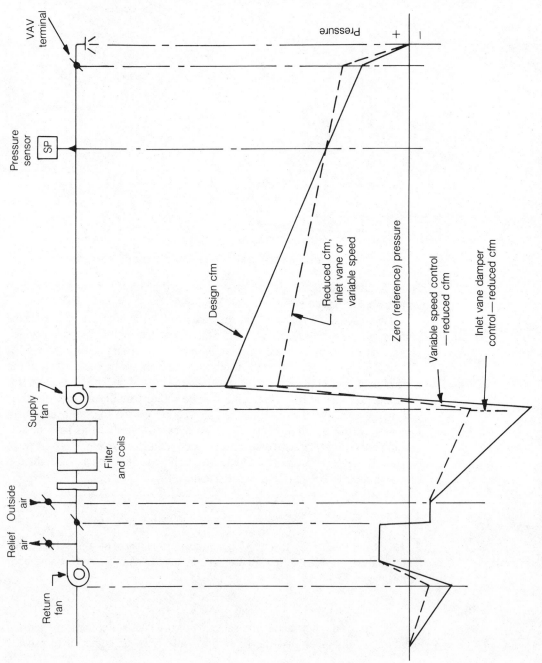

Fig. 3-29. Pressure profiles—inlet vane dampers versus variable speed control.

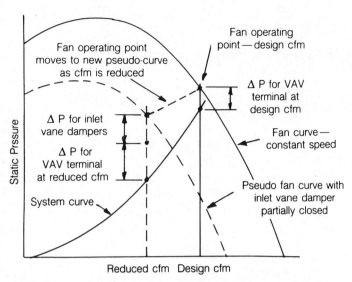

Fig. 3-30. Fan and system curves—inlet vane damper control.

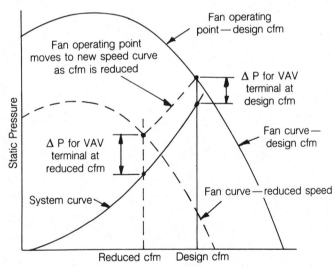

Fig. 3-31. Fan and system curves—fan speed control.

the needed pressure at the most remote terminal. And be sure that the sensor is accessible for maintenance.

See discussions about return fans in this part of the book.

There is another method of controlling system volume that is not discussed here. This involves the use of a bypass duct with a modulating damper.

The fan provides a constant volume air flow, and some air is bypassed directly to the return duct in order to vary the supply to the system. This, of course, saves no energy, but is used on small systems where the cost of a speed controller or inlet vane damper might be excessive.

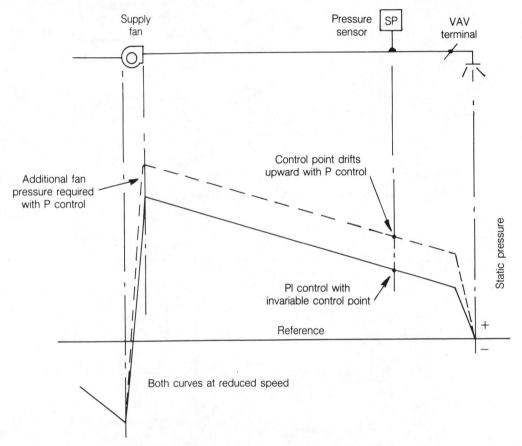

Fig. 3-32. Pressure profiles — P versus PI control.

Air conditioning control for a condominium building*

A reader writes

"We jointly own a beach-front condominium building in Puerto Rico. Electricity rates are $0.12 per kilowatt hour and rising. There are 27 large units (two to the floor) in the 15-story building. (Actually, there are 14 floors with the penthouse, but floor 13 is called 14 — we are superstitious.)

"Each apartment is cooled by a central air conditioning unit. It is a five-ton unit with a 2000 cubic feet per minute fan. The condenser in each unit is cooled by chilled water from a central water cooling tower on the roof. The roof unit is shared by all the apartments but runs day and night, 365 days per year, with two water pumps (one in use and one spare) and four fans (two in use and two spares), using approximately 97 amperes at 208 volts continuously. This costs us approximately $1750 per month.

"We would like the cooling tower to use power reflecting demand. In the summer demand is high during the day and less at night. It is not required in apartments that are not occupied.

"Our estimate is that one-tenth of the capacity is needed in the winter. Even in the summer we think the capacity is excessive. Some people live in the building only in the winter. Others turn the air conditioning off while they work; some, I suppose, suffer the heat.

"We want to use as much circulation pressure and general water chilling as the demand requires. The solution could sense pressure, water temperature or even thermostat settings (on/off), but a self-contained solution on the roof would be best. The building is heavy concrete, making wiring from the individual units to the roof possibly expensive because of the difficulty of installation.

"The solution to our problem should:

1. Be easy to test for proper functioning and easy to maintain.
2. Not require lifting heavy equipment to the roof.
3. Lengthen the life of the roof units, if possible, and stand the corrosion of the sea air.
4. Not require extensive apartment modifications.

"We would appreciate your ideas on a solution. We are convinced that there is no local capability to solve the problem."

Roger Haines replies

The system described by the reader would look something like that shown in FIG. 3-33. This is similar to the central chilled water plant system as described in chapter 12 of reference 1 at the end of this section. An important

---

*October 1983.

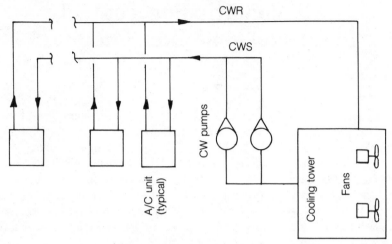

Fig. 3-33. Existing condensing water system.

difference is that a cooling tower will accept a varying water flow rate with no problems, while a chiller will not.

There are four elements to be controlled:

1. Flow to the individual air conditioning unit condensers.
2. CWS (condensing water supply) temperature.
3. Overall flow rate of the CWS (pumping rate).
4. System pumping pressure, which must always be adequate to supply the end-of-line unit.

Air conditioning units   If any diversity and energy saving is to be obtained, each of the units must be provided with an automatic flow control valve in the CW (condensing water) supply or return. Preferably, this will be a two-way (straight-through) valve to allow some savings in pumping costs. The valve should modulate in response to refrigerant head pressure, FIG. 3-34.

Flow rate and pressure   The total water flow rate and pressure tend to vary as the individual control valves modulate. If the pump operates at

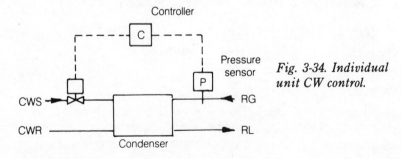

Fig. 3-34. Individual unit CW control.

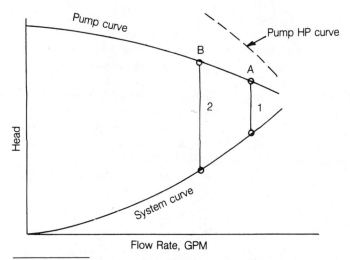

1. Pressure drop through condenser and control valve at design flow.
2. Pressure drop through condenser and control valve at modulated flow.

Fig. 3-35. Pump and system curves — no main flow control.

constant speed and no further control is provided, the result will be as shown in FIG. 3-35. *Pressure drop through the condenser and control valve* represents the composite effect of 27 units on the total flow. Individual flow rates could vary from zero to design maximum. The pump would simply see the net flow and pressure at point B, and this would result in a small decrease in pump horsepower from design point A without any additional control.

If a pressure activated bypass valve is provided between supply and return mains, FIG. 3-36, then the valve will modulate to maintain the pump design condition, point A of FIG. 3-35, and no pump energy will be saved. However, maintenance of a constant main pressure will allow the individual units to control more accurately.

Fig. 3-36. Bypass valve control.

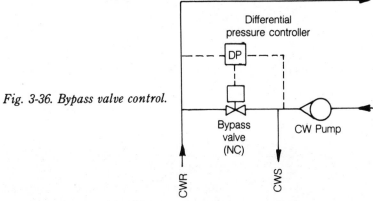

Variable speed pumping, based on maintaining a constant supply-to-return main pressure differential, FIG. 3-37, would result in the curves shown in FIG. 3-38. The heads at points A and B would be the same, to accommodate those units requiring full flow. Horsepower savings would be greater than those obtained in FIG. 3-35. Pump speed controllers would be required, so the economics of FIGS. 3-35 and 3-38 must be carefully evaluated.

Condensing water supply   Because the CWS temperature is a function of web-bulb temperature, water flow and air flow rate on the cooling tower, some control must be provided if an optimum temperature is to be maintained. Because water flow is controlled by the unit valves and wet-bulb temperature is out of your hands, air flow is the only variable you can use.

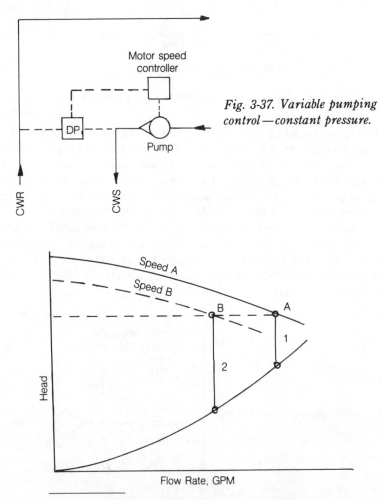

Fig. 3-37. Variable pumping control — constant pressure.

1. Pressure drop through condenser and control valve at design flow.
2. Pressure drop through condenser and control valve at modulated flow.

Fig. 3-38. Pump and system curves — variable-speed pumping.

Air flow rate can be controlled by means of modulating dampers, which save little, if any, fan energy. For energy savings, cycling of the tower fans, either simultaneously or in sequence, is a simple and effective approach. A fairly broad range of CWS temperatures is acceptable, so that wide control differentials can be used to prevent short cycling. A simple dual-temperature water sensor will provide adequate control, FIG. 3-39. This is a typical cooling tower control.

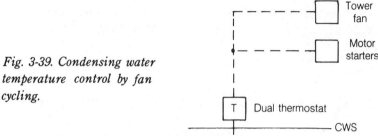

Fig. 3-39. Condensing water temperature control by fan cycling.

There are some interesting problems in interlocking the pump and fan starters and controls to provide automatic changeover to backup. When the standby pump and fans are to be used, some kind of transfer switches and valving must be provided.

Note that none of these control suggestions requires any direct interconnection between the individual units and the cooling tower/pump equipment. The system hydraulic and temperature response provides an adequate source of data.

Reference

1. R.W. Haines, *Control Systems for Heating, Ventilating, and Air Conditioning*, (Fourth Edition), Van Nostrand Reinhold, 1987.

*   *   *

The reply drew the following comment from a reader:

"Valving water flow based on head pressure almost guarantees constant head pressure and this almost certainly must be at peak summertime high temperatures. The savings in fan horsepower of the central system must be offset partially by the lost potential for reduced compressor kilowatts at the satellite units.

"Summer or winter, at partial cooling tower load, the tower leaving water temperature would be lower than it would be with all the satellite units operating. Also, the additional regulating valves would add to the pumping head at design flow.

"System performance must be studied in more detail than the facts given permit. It is possible that the true net savings in the cooling tower system would be greater per system remaining in operation than the potential for savings at the compressors with colder water.

"A full-flow solenoid valve in the water line leaving condenser might produce maximum savings. This valve would close when the compressor stops, open when it starts, and maintain a flooded condenser for startup. The fewer the units operating, the more flow they would get with this at lowest overall head pressure. At the very least, the head pressure operated valve should be moved to the leaving water side of the condenser, as mentioned.

"From manufacturer's catalogs, the reduction of condensing temperature from 120 to 90 degrees F saves 20 percent in kilowatts per ton of refrigeration."

Control strategies for VAV systems*

Controls for variable air volume (VAV) systems include five principal subsystems: local space temperature, supply fan volume, matching supply and return fan volumes, supply air temperature, and economy cycle control of outside air volume.

Although all of these have often been discussed in print, it might be helpful to take an integrated look, keeping in mind the interrelationships among these elements and some of the problems that have arisen with VAV systems.

On an annual basis, a VAV system will have a lower fan energy requirement than other types of air handling systems. (See reference 1 at the end of this section.) This is due to the reduction in fan work at part load as air flow is reduced. However, air flow reduction can give rise to a number of problems:

1. Too great a reduction in air flow can lead to poor air distribution, inadequate ventilation, and high humidity, with many complaints from occupants. (See reference 2 at the end of this section.)
2. If direct expansion cooling is used, then decreasing air flow across the coil can lead to icing and poor control of air temperature. (See reference 3 at the end of this section.)
3. Decreasing the air flow rate across any heat transfer coil can make control more difficult because of changes in system gains. (See reference 4 at the end of this section.)
4. In any VAV system the available static pressure will vary widely from one terminal to another. Some means of compensation must be used if good zone control is to be obtained.
5. There is no accepted simple and inexpensive way of controlling return fan volume to track supply fan volume.

Thus it is evident that VAV, like every other solution, is not foolproof or

*September 1984.

automatic. Use it with discretion and understanding. With this in mind, look at the subsystems in some detail.

Space temperature control

With a VAV system, space temperature is controlled by varying the volume rather than the temperature of the supply air. The control device is called a *terminal* or *box* and is essentially a motorized volume damper. If it is not compensated for variations in duct static pressure—and these will occur —accurate control is difficult. Most boxes are compensated in one of two ways. In FIG. 3-40 a flow (velocity) sensor/controller controls the damper to maintain a constant flow corresponding to its setpoint. That setpoint is reset by the space temperature sensor. In FIG. 3-41 the damper motor is controlled directly from the space thermostat, with a mechanical device—usually a spring— arranged to compensate for pressure variations.

To avoid the distribution and ventilation problems associated with low air flow rates (problem 1) designers recommend a minimum setting below which the damper is not allowed to close farther. Recommendations vary from 30 to 50 percent; I prefer 40 to 50 percent. At light load conditions, this might require that the supply air temperature be raised to avoid overcooling (see the discussions that follow).

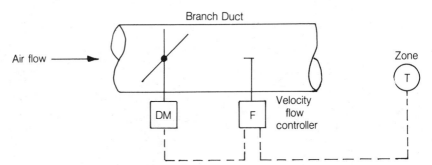

Fig. 3-40. Zone volume control with velocity compensation.

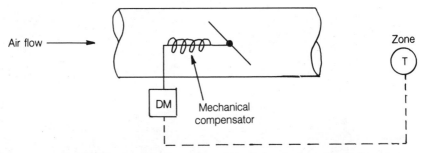

Fig. 3-41. Zone volume control with mechanical compensation.

Supply fan volume

As the terminal dampers modulate the total supply air volume will change. There are several ways of adjusting the supply fan volume to match. (See reference 5 at the end of this section.) The most effective, from an energy conservation standpoint, are inlet vane dampers and fan speed control. Either of these is controlled to maintain a constant static pressure at some point in the supply duct. (For a detailed discussion, see reference 5 at the end of this section or some of the many articles on this subject published in the last few years.)

Matching supply and return air fan volume

This is perhaps the most difficult and controversial area in VAV. Generally, the return air volume is less than the supply air volume by the amount required to make up fixed exhaust and pressurize the building. In the simplest arrangement, FIG. 3-42, both fans are controlled by a single static pressure controller in the supply duct. This control reduces both fan volumes in the same proportion, so the absolute difference between the volumes decreases as the total volume decreases. This means that exhaust and makeup air are no longer in balance and control has been lost. An effective way of compensating

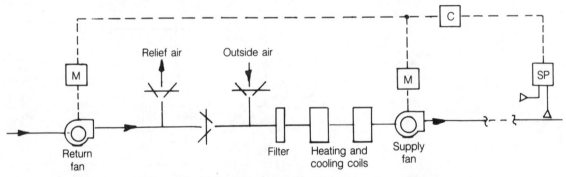

Fig. 3-42. Fan tracking with a single sensor/controller.

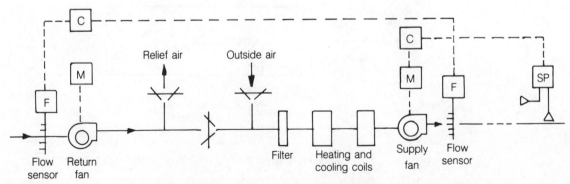

Fig. 3-43. Fan tracking with air flow measurement.

for this is by means of air flow measuring stations, FIG. 3-43, which accurately measure the supply and return air flow rates and adjust fan volumes to maintain the desired absolute difference. This is the most costly control system but it works well.

Somewhere between in cost effectiveness is the system shown in FIG. 3-44. (See reference 6 at the end of this section.) This system uses separate static pressure controllers for the supply and return fans, resetting the return fan controller to maintain the absolute difference in the two air volumes. The problem with this is finding a good location for the return static pressure sensing tip. The mixed air plenum would be the preferred location but air flow in this plenum tends to be very turbulent. Figure 3-44 shows a solution that has been used successfully, with the sensing tip located downstream of the filter where the air flow is relatively stable. This can be affected by the change in pressure drop through the filter as it gets dirty. Also, it is necessary to put a minimum stop on the return air damper to prevent closure beyond about 5 percent open. This concept is simple and comparatively inexpensive. Another option is to use a relief fan instead of a return air fan, FIG. 3-45. This works only if the return air system is short and has a low pressure loss. The relief fan and damper can be controlled from building pressure.

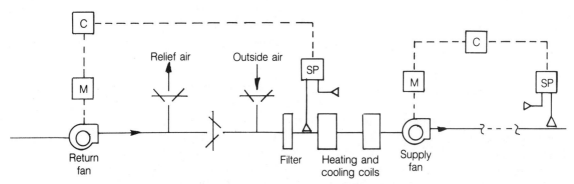

Fig. 3-44. Fan tracking with two static pressure controllers.

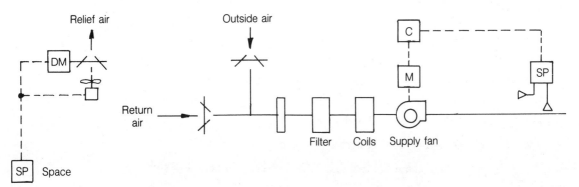

Fig. 3-45. Supply-return air balance with relief fan control.

Supply air temperature

The usual procedure with VAV is to provide a constant air temperature all year. This procedure is not necessarily the most economical or best procedure. As noted, it might be desirable to raise the supply air temperature during periods of light load to maintain adequate air movement and ventilation rates. This strategy causes the fan to use more energy, but it also allows energy savings in other areas. For example, if the supply air temperature is raised, the chilled water temperature can also be raised, with an improvement in chiller plant efficiency. If the outdoor temperature is low enough, it might be possible to eliminate or minimize the use of chilled water.

Economy cycle control of outside air

Economy cycle control with VAV is the same as with any other type of HVAC system with one significant difference. On the minimum outside air cycle, as the supply fan volume decreases, so will the outside air volume. Therefore, it is necessary to do one of two things:

1. Increase the design minimum outside air volume so that at minimum supply air volume the outside air volume will still be adequate to meet ventilation codes and requirements.
2. Add a volume flow sensor in the outside air to maintain the design minimum at all conditions of the supply air volume.

The second solution is better from an energy-use standpoint but complicates the control system. The tradeoff needs to be investigated for each system.

You have looked at some of the problems encountered with VAV systems and ways of handling these problems with the various control subsystems. These are suggestions that come from practice and experience. These are not necessarily the only systems nor even the best. As a designer, you need to investigate every system to find the best or, at least, acceptable answers.

References

1. William Tao, "ATF: Air Transport Factor," *Heating/Piping/Air Conditioning*, April 1984, pages 95–100.

2. R.H. Morris and M.E. Wiggin, "Indoor Air Pollution," unpublished.

3. W.J. Coad, "DX Control Problems with VAV," *Heating/Piping/Air Conditioning*, January 1984, pages 134 and 139.

4. R.W. Haines, "System Gains," in part 2 of this book.

5. _____, "Supply Fan Volume Control in a VAV System," in part 3 of this book.

6. _____, "Supply and Return Air Fan Control in a VAV System," in part 3 of this book.

*   *   *

As noted in the comments to references 5 and 6, there are a great many engineers/designers in favor of never using return fans in a VAV system. My own opinion is that *never* is too strong a term, but I avoid return fans except under exceptional circumstances.

There is another method of controlling minimum outside air volume: use a minimum outside air fan — with the desired volume and a very low pressure rise. This will still allow the economy cycle to function.

Temperature and humidity control for electronic manufacturing*

One of the oldest theological trivia questions is, "How many angels can stand on the head of a pin?" Whatever answer the church fathers finally agreed upon, it is doubtful that it was any greater quantity than the number of electronic circuits modern technology can put on a tiny solid-state chip.

The manufacturing of these LSI (large-scale integrated) circuit devices is the key to the present state-of-the-art in computer design. Because of the small size and high purity requirements, the manufacturing environment must be controlled very carefully. Typically, a Class 10,000 clean room environment is needed, with a relative humidity of 35 to 40 percent and a temperature of 70 to 72 degrees F.

These numbers represent an allowable design range but, once selected, the design conditions must be maintained within very close tolerances — for example, plus or minus 3 percent relative humidity and plus or minus 1 degree F. Some parts of the process will accept plus or minus 5 percent relative humidity and plus or minus 2 degrees F. These conditions must be maintained so that manufacturing quality requirements can be met.

An additional factor is that to maintain clean room conditions a large volume of air flow is required — on the order of 8 to 10 cubic feet per minute per square foot. This means that there will be only a small difference between entering air and space temperatures. But the cooling coil leaving air temperature must be very low to satisfy the humidity requirements. Thus, considerable reheat is needed. The manufacturing process also requires large amounts of exhaust air, typically on the order of 40 percent of supply.

When design cooling conditions are plotted on a psychrometric chart the result could be as shown in FIG. 3-46. Assumed design conditions are: outside, 100 degrees F dry bulb, 74 degrees F wet bulb; space, 70 degrees F dry bulb, 40 percent relative humidity; outside air for exhaust makeup, 40 percent of

---

*November 1984.

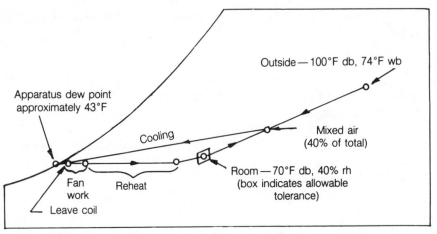

Fig. 3-46. Psychrometric chart — summer design conditions.

total air; and a draw-through air handling system with a 4 degree F rise due to fan work. Observing the large amount of reheat, you can see the need for heat recovery or some energy reclaim procedure. The large amount of outside air suggests the possibility of precooling with some more energy-efficient method than mechanical refrigeration. The need for a 43 degree F apparatus dew point means that ordinary 40 degree F chilled water will not be adequate, and a brine solution at about 35 degree F will be needed.

All of this is at maximum design cooling conditions, which must be met but which prevail for only a few hours each year. Figure 3-47 is the psychrometric chart for an outside condition of 70 degrees F dry bulb and 60 percent relative humidity. Outdoor conditions of 60 to 80 degrees F prevail for 40 to 50 percent of the operating hours in most locations in the continental United States. The situation in FIG. 3-47 is that the overall cooling load had decreased but the reheat is still the same.

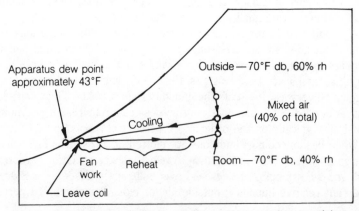

Fig. 3-47. Psychrometric chart — intermediate outside conditions.

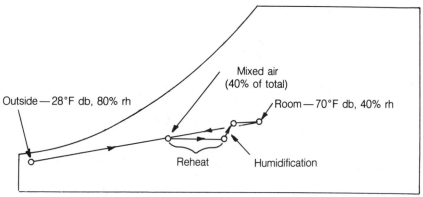

Fig. 3-48. Psychrometric chart — winter design conditions.

Figure 3-48 is the psychrometric chart for a winter outdoor condition of 28 degrees F dry bulb and 80 percent relative humidity. Less reheat is required but humidity must now be added.

These analyses on psychrometric charts enable you to better understand the process and to develop procedures for satisfying the design conditions with a minimum expenditure of energy. A number of solutions are possible. The designer has plenty of opportunities to be ingenious. One solution was described some time ago. (See reference 1 at the end of this section.) There are interesting possibilities in chemical dehumidification. The solution which follows is simply one possibility that can be used if circumstances warrant.

In the situation discussed here, two additional criteria exist: the conditioned spaces are to be maintained at a positive pressure of 0.15 inches of water (gauge), plus or minus 0.02 inches, with respect to contiguous spaces, and the facility is to have its own chiller plant.

Figure 3-49 shows the supply air arrangement. One air system serves three zones, so each zone has a reheat coil, a humidifier, and a volume damper for controlling the zone pressure as exhaust quantities vary, and doors open and close. It is desirable to have air locks to make the pressures more controllable.

The system includes a precooler in the outside air. This is a secondary effect evaporate cooler. Such a system, when properly maintained, will achieve a temperature drop in the outside air of 60 percent or more of the difference between entering dry and wet bulb temperatures. Instead of the precooler, a runaround heat-recovery coil system could have been used between the exhaust and outside air streams.

The clean room environment forces the use of high-efficiency bag filters plus HEPA (high-efficiency absolute filter) final filters.

The cooling coil is controlled to provide a constant leaving air temperature of 45 degrees F. This should provide the needed specific humidity, but the controls are arranged to allow any one of the zone humidity sensors to override if the zone humidity increases above the setpoint.

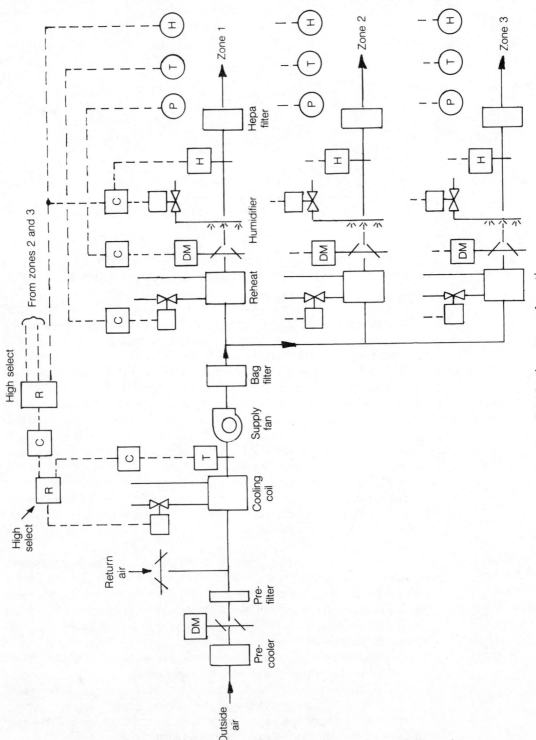

Fig. 3-49. Supply-air system schematic.

The zone humidity sensor, in addition to override control of the cooling coil, provides for control of the humidifier valve to add humidity when needed. A duct high-limit humidity sensor is used to avoid condensation in the duct.

A zone air-supply volume damper is controlled by the pressure in the zone. Because the volume changes will be small, the fan volume need not be controlled—the fan will accommodate by riding up the curve.

Not shown on the diagram, but highly desirable, is indication of status for critical temperatures, humidities and pressures.

Because the HVAC system has its own chiller plant, the condensing water can be used for reheat as shown in FIG. 3-50. Two chillers are used to allow the chilled water system to function efficiently at light loads. In normal operation, the reheat coils will use half or more of the condensing heat; the rest must be rejected through a closed-circuit water cooler. The differential pressure from supply to return is used to modulate flow through the cooler. The water temperature leaving the cooler is used to control the cooler spray pump and fan. During cold weather, the chillers might be off or operating at very light load. Then at least one condensing water pump will run, and the boiler will provide the necessary heat. All of this requires a rather complex control interlock system to ensure flow of condensing and chiller water where and as needed. Details of the system are not included here. This is an excellent application for a direct digital controller.

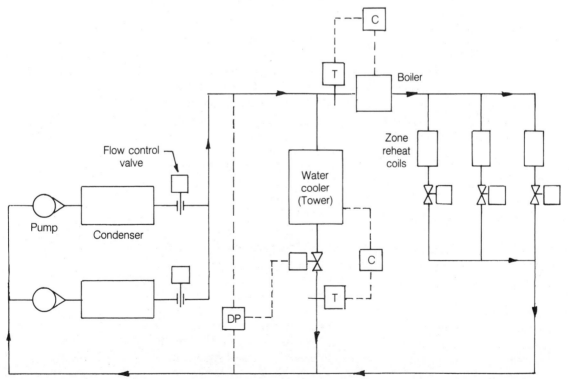

Fig. 3-50. Condensing/reheat water schematic.

The sensors and controllers must have a high degree of accuracy and reliability. To control to plus or minus 5 percent relative humidity, the sensor must have an accuracy of plus or minus 3 percent or better. This means an industrial quality instrument and PI (proportional-plus-integral) control. Similarly, the temperature sensor must have an accuracy two or three times as good as the design requirement.

As noted above, there are other possible solutions. Chemical dehumidification can change the whole process. Or a sprayed coil dehumidifier can be used for part of the precooling/reheating process. Only a careful analysis, together with a careful study of local conditions and practices and the client's preferences, can result in an optimum solution.

Reference

1. R.W. Haines, "Control for Low Humidity," in part 3 of this book.

Humidity sensors, three-duct multizone, standard protocol*

Humidity sensors

One of the more difficult control problems is that of controlling humidity. Manufacturing processes, particularly in electronics, have become increasingly dependent on control of temperature and humidity within close limits.

No control system is better than its sensor. Humidity sensors of the quality and accuracy required for these close tolerances have traditionally been available only at prices considerable above those for commercial sensors. The price differential still exists but is not so great any more because, in part, of the same electronic developments that require the close control.

One new type of relative humidity sensor is made by several manufacturers and is reasonably priced. This is the thin-film capacitance type. The basic element is a 1 or 2 micron layer of absorbent di-electric polymer. Arranged as a capacitor, the film absorbance varies, so does the capacitance. The sensor includes an amplifier and transmitter, so that the transmitted signal is proportional to relative humidity. Accuracy is plus or minus 3 percent which is adequate for humidity control to plus or minus 5 percent. A similar type of instrument using variable resistance is also made.

For even closer control — such as a space requirement of plus or minus 3 percent — there is an even better sensor. The chilled-mirror sensor uses a small thermoelectric refrigeration element to cool a metal mirror. A photocell "sees" the reflectance change due to condensation on the mirror when the dew point temperature is reached. The temperature is measured by a platinum

---

*December 1984.

RTD (resistance temperature detector). The system includes an amplifier and transmitter. The result is a signal proportional to dew point temperature with an accuracy better than plus or minus one degree F. The instrument can be equipped with circuitry to convert the signal to relative humidity with an accuracy equal to or better than the solid-state sensor.

Both types of sensors are available in wall or duct mounting arrangements with electronic outputs such as 0–10 volts direct current or 4–20 milliamperes.

Three-duct multizone air-handling system

This system has been proposed as the energy saving alternative to the conventional two-duct constant volume multizone system. Along with the conventional hot and cold ducts, a bypass duct is added, FIG. 3-51. This allows us to avoid the mixing of hot and cold air streams. The control sequence for each zone is as follows:

1. At maximum heating the hot damper is fully open; the other dampers are closed.
2. As the heating requirement decreases, the hot damper modulates toward the closed position, and the bypass damper modulates toward the open position. The cold damper remains closed.
3. At the neutral output of the controller, the bypass is fully open and hot and cold dampers are closed.
4. As the cooling requirement increases, the cold damper modulates toward the open position while the bypass damper modulates toward the closed position. The hot damper remains closed.

Notice that for this sequence, the controller output covers the range from minimum (full heating) to maximum (full cooling) but the bypass damper opens a first, then reverse its action and closes. This can be dealt with using pneumatic controls as shown in FIG. 3-52. Here, the controller output from 3 to 8 pounds per square inch works to modulate the hot and bypass dampers. At 8 pounds per square inch the switching relay transfers the controller output to a

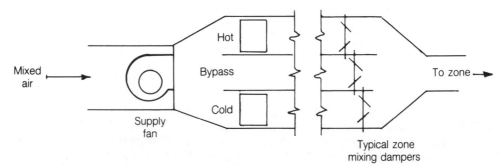

Fig. 3-51. Three-duct, multizone air-handling unit.

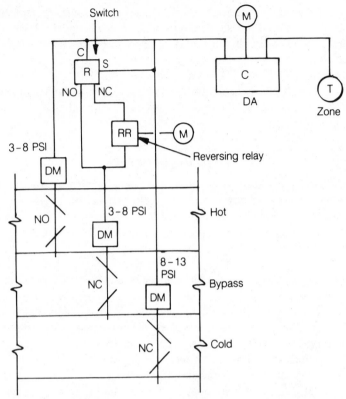

Fig. 3-52. Three-duct multizone — pneumatic controls.

reversing relay which allows the cold and bypass dampers to modulate over the 8 to 13 pounds per square inch controller output range. Electronic controls can be used in a similar manner. A direct digital controller would provide three separate outputs and the switching/reversing relays would not be needed.

Standard protocol

An interesting development is taking place in the process control industry. Programmable controllers and microprocessor control systems have always had the same lack of compatability seen in the HVAC control field. This is primarily because each manufacturer uses a different message structure and communication protocol.

Now General Motors, the largest user of computer base process control systems, has developed a standard MAP (Manufacturing Automation Protocol) specification to which all suppliers of such systems to General Motors must comply. Many manufacturers are announcing compliance and it appears that the process control industry, as a whole, might go along. Efforts are being made to make MAP a concensus standard under IEEE (Institute of Electrical and Electronics Engineers).

A similar standard for HVAC controls does not appear likely. The increasing use of electronic control systems is leading to a great deal of interchangability among the devices of various manufacturers. But the communication protocols remain different.

*   *   *

The three-duct multizone unit can also be controlled as shown in FIG. 3-53. The use of four dampers eliminates the need for the switching and reversing relays, though the basic sequence is still the same.

A standard protocol is still elusive. At least three groups are trying to write such a standard, including an ASHRAE committee. There are many difficulties, both technical and political. Perhaps some day it will happen. MAP has still not become an industry standard.

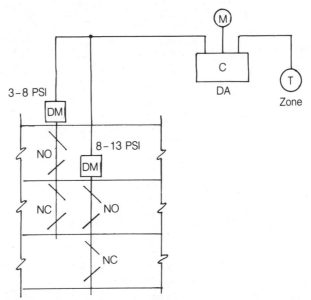

Fig. 3-53. Three-duct multizone — pneumatic controls.

Control of smoke-control systems*

The term *engineered* as applied to smoke control systems implies a greater degree of design sophistication than that required for simple HVAC. In particular, design for smoke control might require larger air quantities than would be needed for air conditioning. Most smoke control systems use zoning principles, exhausting the smoke from the fire zone and pressurizing the adjacent zones to prevent smoke migration. A typical system could be similar to that shown in

*April 1985.

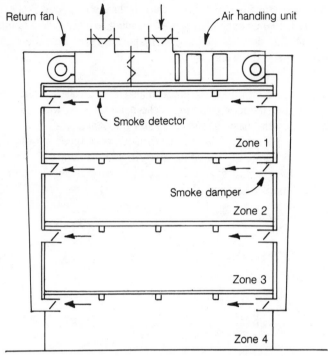

Fig. 3-54. HVAC system with smoke control capability.

FIG. 3-54. Zoning separation may be horizontal, with two or more zones per floor, or vertical, or both.

The basic criteria for control are these:

1. The system should be automatic, activated by fire detectors in the zones. To prevent false alarms two detectors in a zone should be tripped before the system is energized.
2. Upon activation, mixed air dampers at the air handler should go to full outside air and full exhaust. Positive exhaust is needed, either a return fan or a relief fan. The zone smoke dampers for the smoke zone should be open to exhaust and closed to supply, to create a negative pressure. The smoke dampers for other zones, at least those adjacent to the smoke zone, should be open to supply and closed to exhaust to create a positive pressure.
3. If the system is VAV, the fan-volume controls should be switched to maximum.
4. A fire department panel is desirable. This allows the professional firefighters to manually override fan and damper controls if necessary. This panel should also include reliable status indicators for fans and dampers. *Reliable* implies that fan status indicators are based on air flow sensors and damper indicators are based on limit switches. Indicators should also show the smoke zone or zones.

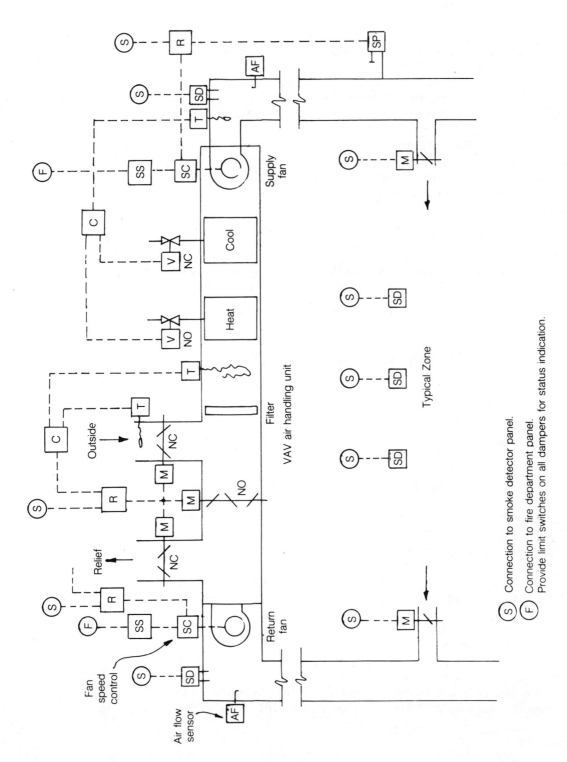

Fig. 3-55. Control of HVAC system for smoke control.

A system that incorporates these criteria is shown schematically in FIG. 3-55. The diagram is generic, with fundamental devices and interconnections shown. Details, such as how the system knows there are two smoke sensors activated in the zone and how the fire department panel can be used to override the local loop, are not shown. This control system could use a computer, or control could be accomplished with electromechanical logic. For large systems, it might be more cost effective to use a computer. These decisions must be made for each system; there are no general rules.

As often emphasized, the controls are only as effective as the system being controlled. If the HVAC system is not properly designed for smoke control, the best controls will not make it effective. Be sure to read the ASHRAE special publication, "Design of Smoke Control Systems for Buildings" (1983).

*   *   *

More smoke control research has been done and more material published since this was written. Principles are still much the same, but more data are available on air flow rates, for example, than before. Most of this is available in ASHRAE publications or the Handbook.

Outside air-volume control in a VAV system*

VAV systems, popular as they are, are not without problems. One of the more serious problems, which has not really been addressed, is the control of minimum outside air quantity in the typical economy cycle.

To refresh your memory, look at the typical economy cycle operation, shown in FIG. 3-56. When the supply fan is running, control power is provided, and the outside air damper opens to at least minimum position. Controller C1, using the information from mixed air sensor T2, controls the dampers to maintain the mixed air temperature at some low limit setpoint — usually 55 to 60 degrees F. As the outside air temperature increases, a larger fraction of outside air is used until 100 percent outside air is obtained. A further rise in outside air temperature — to, say, 70 to 75 degrees F — will cause the high limit thermostat T2 to switch relay R1, blocking the signal from C1. Now the minimum signal, through high select relay R2, controls the dampers and minimum outside air is used.

Another arrangement, FIG. 3-57, uses a separate minimum outside air damper which opens when the fan is running. A maximum outside air damper is modulated to maintain the low limit temperature.

This is fine in a constant-volume system. But, with variable volume, the pressure relationships change as the flow volumes change. At 50 percent total

---

*October 1986.

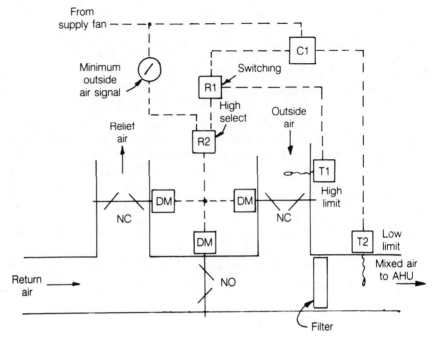

Fig. 3-56. *Typical economy cycle.*

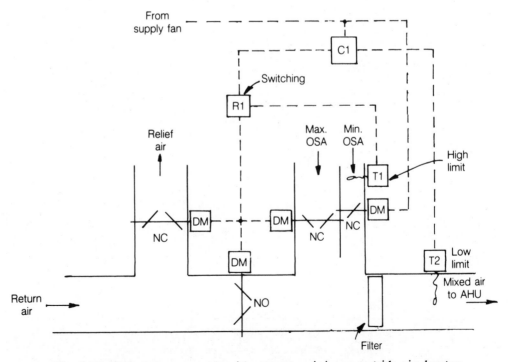

Fig. 3-57. *Typical economy cycle with separate minimum outside air damper.*

flow through the air handling unit, the flow through the outside damper will be less than design, though not necessarily in the same ratio. Then the code and comfort requirements for ventilation rates probably will not be met.

This problem is aggravated when return fans are used, another reason why return fans are disliked by so many designers.

The following alternative solutions appear feasible:

1. Increase the minimum outside air volume setting. An increase to twice the code requirement should ensure that sufficient outside air is provided, even at air handling unit flows as low as 40 percent of design. This requires no change in the control system, though the minimum outside air damper of FIG. 3-57 would have to be increased in size. A serious drawback would be the increase in energy consumption due to the increased use of outside air.
2. Provide an airflow measuring device in the minimum outside air stream, FIG. 3-58. This can be a simple velocity sensor, calibrated to the appropriate velocity at design conditions. Controller C2 uses the velocity signal to provide a control signal through high select relay R2

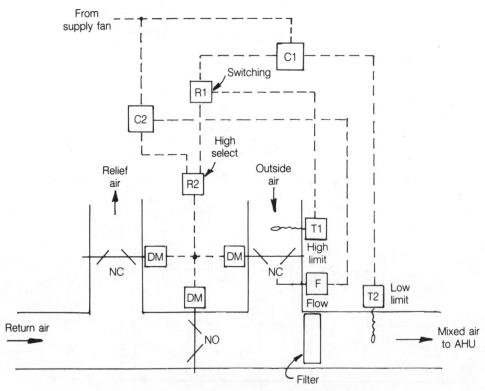

Fig. 3-58. Economy cycle with flow sensor for minimum outside air.

to the damper operators. Thus a constant minimum flow of outside air will be provided at all times, regardless of the air handling unit flow. When the output of C1 exceeds that of C2, the system will be controlled as before, to satisfy the low limit mixed air temperature.

Figure 3-59 shows the same concept applied to the system with a separate minimum outside air damper.

This alternative would use much less energy than the first, at the expense of two additional control devices and an increase in control complexity.

References

1. Robert Morris and Merlon Wiggin, "Indoor Air Pollution," *Heating/Piping/Air Conditioning*, February 1985, page 73.

2. Dan Int-Hout and Phil Berger, "What's Really Wrong with VAV Systems," *ASHRAE Journal*, December 1984, page 36.

3. Gil Avery, "VAV Economizer Cycle: Don't Use a Return Air Fan," *Heating/Piping/Air Conditioning*, August 1984, page 91.

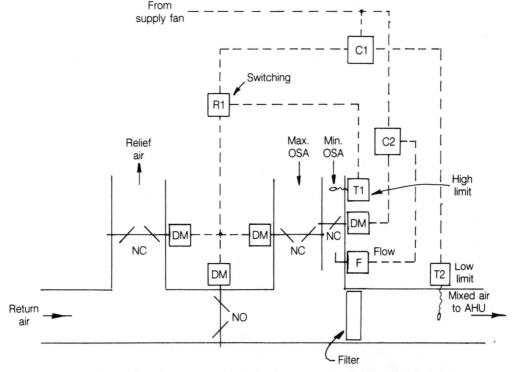

Fig. 3-59. Economy cycle with flow sensor for minimum outside air.

Double-duct systems*

A DD (double-duct) system utilizes the multizone principle of providing parallel hot and cold air streams and mixing the streams to provide zone control. Thus, heating in one zone and cooling in another can be provided simultaneously, FIG. 3-60. Multizone systems are limited by the need for a "home-run" duct for each zone. The DD system extends the hot and cold plenums throughout the building, allowing, in theory, an infinite number of zones. It also provides flexibility in that zones can be added or changed without great expense. It is also possible to use smaller ducts by increasing duct velocity and pressure drop. This makes architects and builders happy, since the building floor-to-floor height can be minimized.

The system has much to recommend it from a control standpoint but, because it is a reheat type system, it is very wasteful of energy.

Double-duct air conditioning systems began to be used extensively in about the mid 1950s. Many systems were designed and installed in the 1950s and 1960s when energy was cheap. The economic advantage of smaller ducts was emphasized so much that many systems were designed for total pressures of 8 to 10 inches of water (gauge) across the supply fan. It is interesting to note that in these very high pressure systems, the fan energy can exceed the thermal energy on an annual basis.

The energy crisis put a stop to all this, and present day energy codes essentially outlaw the traditional system of FIG. 3-60. It is, however, possible to design a DD system that is as energy efficient as VAV and is, in some respects, superior to VAV. Figure 3-61 illustrates the two-fan DD system, with VAV as an added feature.

One of the difficulties with the single-fan DD system is the wide variation in flow between the hot and cold ducts, which changes seasonally. This requires pressure compensated mixing boxes and even pressure control dampers in the duct mains. The variable-volume feature of the two-fan system does away with this problem and provides all of the fan work energy savings associated with conventional VAV.

Another difficulty with the single fan DD is the setting of the mixed or low-limit controller in the outside air economy cycle. If this is set low enough to save cooling energy, it adds to the reheat load in the hot duct. Annualized energy studies indicate that a considerable savings can be obtained by resetting the mixed air temperature upward in colder weather. But in an office building with large interior zone areas, that might be counter productive, because the interior zone cooling load is essentially independent of outdoor temperature. The two-fan DD system overcomes this shortcoming by using the mixed air primarily or entirely on the cold-duct side, with the hot-duct side using primarily warm return air. It can be argued that the heated zones receive less primary ventilation air, but ventilation, as a whole, is adequate and meets code and good practice requirements.

---

*January 1987.

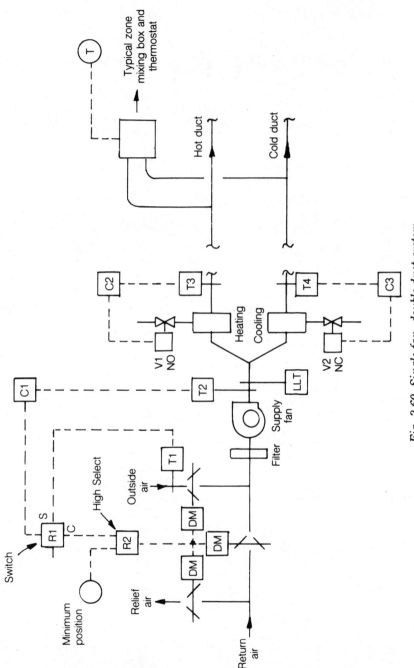

Fig. 3-60. Single-fan, double-duct system.

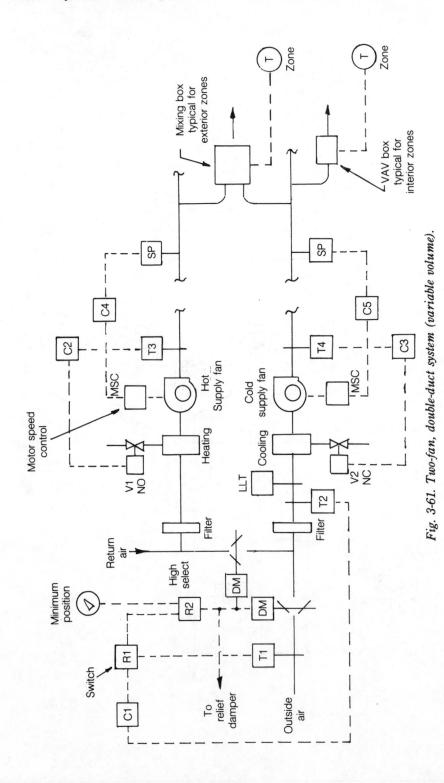

Fig. 3-61. Two-fan, double-duct system (variable volume).

Because heating is needed primarily on the exterior zones, these zones are provided with mixing boxes with hot and cold connections. Interior zones, which need only cooling, are served through VAV boxes.

The net result is an energy efficient system with all the control advantages of double duct and the energy conservation advantages of VAV and economy cycle.

A brilliant, new, innovative idea? Hardly. A leading proponent for this type of system was the late Fred McFadden, one of the first to use double-duct systems in the 1950s. The only thing he lacked was the reliable, inexpensive motor speed controls now available. To quote axiom of this column: "Fundamentals don't change."

*   *   *

It is also possible to make this a complete VAV system by using variable-volume mixing boxes on the exterior zones. The control cycle for such a box provides for full-design cooling flow (in cubic feet per minute) at maximum cooling load, gradually reducing to some minimum flow as cooling load decreases. At the minimum flow, the cold damper might continue to close while the hot damper starts to modulate open to maintain the minimum flow. As heating load increases the hot damper might modulate open to allow full design flow heating flow; the cold damper has long since closed.

Part 4

Control devices

Most of this book deals with theory, philosophy, or applications. There are only a few sections in this part of the book, and the information presented is general. The section on valves is very important; incorrect selection of valves is a cause of many "poor control" problems. In general, the criteria for selection of control devices should be accuracy—not only initial accuracy but continuing—and reliability. The degree of accuracy needed depends to some extent on the application, but note that people are expecting a more comfortable environment than was previously acceptable. Many industrial and institutional processes require a much higher degree of accuracy than those expected in commercial HVAC applications. So, read catalog data carefully and insist on good information on long-term accuracy and reliability. A statement such as: "these devices can be field calibrated to an xxx degree of accuracy" is not usually acceptable, because good field calibration is difficult and time consuming and tells nothing about long-term accuracy. The best control system design will be wasted if the devices cannot do the job.

Control valve selection*

The selection of a control valve for heating or cooling seems like a very simple process. Just pick a valve that will pass the required flow rate at a reasonable pressure drop. But what is "reasonable?" How does the valve pressure drop relate to the system and the ability of the valve to control? This article will discuss the hydraulics of the situation and consider the effect of various valve/system pressure relationships.

Control valve flow capacities are expressed in terms of the pressure drop across the valve and the flow coefficient, C_v, which is a function of the valve size and design. The general equation for fluid flow is:

$$Q = C_v \, (h)^{1/2} \tag{4-1}$$

where: Q = flow rate, gpm or lb per hr
h = pressure drop, psi

Thus, a valve having a C_v of 5 (for water) would pass 10 gallons per minute at a pressure drop of 4 pounds per square inch. Note that the value of C_v will vary depending on the fluid used — steam, water, gas, or air, for example. Values are provided by the valve manufacturer.

Control valves used in HVAC work generally have either *linear* or *equal percentage* plugs, as shown in FIG. 4-1. With the linear plug, the C_v varies linearly with the plug *lift* (travel from closed to open). With the equal percentage plug, C_v varies in an exponential fashion. With a second-power function, for example, if the valve closes to 50 percent of lift the C_v for a linear plug would be approximately 50 percent of the fully open C_v; For an equal percentage valve, the C_v would be about 25 percent. Other characteristics are available, but are not usual in HVAC work.

In practice, the valve curves do not quite match the ideal. Figure 4-1 shows typical manufacturer's curves compared to the theoretical curves.

Figure 4-2 shows a simple coil and control valve system. For simplicity, assume the available pressure differential between supply and return mains (ΔP_m) to be fixed, regardless of what happens to the flow rate through the coil. The coil and its associated piping (except the control valve) constitute a small system, and in accordance with the laws of hydraulics, the pressure drop through the system varies as the square of the flow, as indicated in FIG. 4-3:

$$\Delta P_1/\Delta P_2 = (Q_1/Q_2)^2 \tag{4-2}$$

In practice this is not quite true because of restrictions and turbulence, but it is sufficiently accurate for most purposes.

Now, if you superimpose the system curve of FIG. 4-3 on a graph that also includes the ΔP between the mains and the control valve pressure drop, we get something like FIG. 4-4. In this figure, at any flow rate, the sum of the

---

*September 1980.

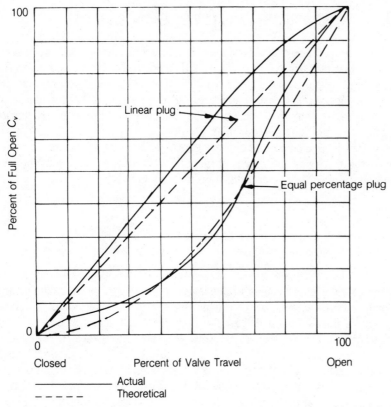

Fig. 4-1. C$_v$ for typical control valves (Basis: Fisher, type BF, 1^1/$_2$ in. size.

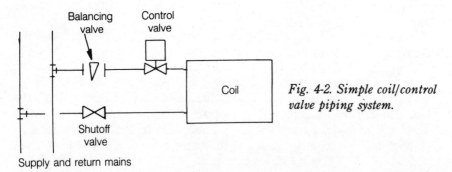

Fig. 4-2. Simple coil/control valve piping system.

system pressure drop, ΔP_s, and the valve pressure drop, ΔP_v, must equal the main pressure differential, ΔP_m. However, the design ratio of ΔP_v to ΔP_s has a considerable effect on the way the system controls. More explicitly, it affects the valve travel required to achieve decreased flow rates, and therefore, the ability of the valve to control effectively at part load.

Consider an example:

Assume ΔP_v is to be selected to equal one-half of ΔP_s: Let ΔP_s equal 8 pounds per square inch (26.5 feet of water) at the design flow rate. Then ΔP_v

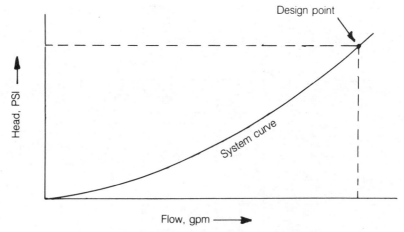

Fig. 4-3. System curve — flow versus head.

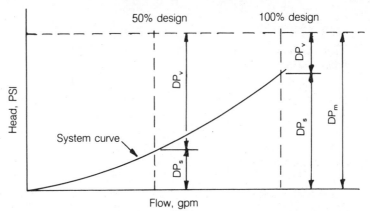

Fig. 4-4. DP$_s$ *and* DP$_v$ *at 100 and 50 percent of design flow.*

equals 4 pounds per square inch and ΔP_m equals 12 pounds per square inch. If the flow rate is 20 gallons per minute the C_v for the valve must be 20 divided by $4^{\frac{1}{2}}$, or 10.0 (Catalogs will indicate about a 1¼-inch valve size).

Now if the load decreases to a point where a flow rate of 10 gallons per minute (50 percent of design) is needed, the system ΔP will decrease to one-fourth its design value, or 2 pounds per square inch. Since ΔP_m remains constant at 12 pounds per square inch, the valve pressure drop must increase to 10 pounds per square inch — 2½ times its original value. Then the valve C_v must be 10 divided by $10^{\frac{1}{2}}$, which equals 3.16. This represents a decrease of 68 percent in the value of C_v.

If the flow rate is further reduced to 6 gallons per minute (30 percent of design), ΔP_s equals 9 percent of the original design — 0.72 pounds per square inch. Then ΔP_v equals 11.28 psi and C_v equals 1.79 — a decrease of 82 percent. This requires an equal percentage plug to close to about 48 percent open, while a linear plug would only be 18 percent open.

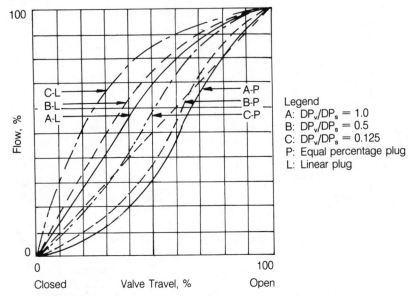

Fig. 4-5. Flow rate versus valve travel for linear and equal percentage plugs at various design values of DP_v/DP_s.

If calculations like these are made for flow rates at 10 percent increments and with initial design ratios of $\Delta P_v : \Delta P_s$ of 1.0, 0.5, and 0.125, the results can be plotted as a function of percent flow vs. percent valve travel. Figure 4-5 shows the curves for the linear and equal percentage valves.

The conclusions to be drawn are as follows:

1. The linear plug valve does not control as well as the equal percentage valve. At high flow rates, a large valve travel is required to achieve any effective change in flow. At low flow rates, a small amount of travel has a large effect on flow.
2. The equal percentage valve with a design ratio of $\Delta P_v : \Delta P_s$ of 0.5 or higher has a nearly linear effect on flow at high rates. At low flow rates, valve travel percentage is greater than flow change percentage, providing good control.
3. A low design ratio of $\Delta P_v : \Delta P_s$ causes the equal percentage valve curve to approach the shape of the linear control valve.
4. Better control is achieved with $\Delta P_v : \Delta P_s$ design ratios of 0.5 or higher, but increasing the design ratio above 0.5 does not improve control a great deal. Since less pump head — and energy — is needed at the lower design ratio, a value of 0.5 would appear optimum.

In making this analysis I made the simplifying assumption that supply to return main pressure drop was always constant. In real life, of course, this situation would be very unusual except perhaps in a large system with variable speed pumping. It is also true that the change in flow rate is not directly proportional to the change in coil capacity. And certainly the valve travel relates not only to the output signal from the thermostat, but also to the valve spring range.

It does not appear that any of these factors will really affect the qualitative validity of these results. This kind of analysis is always helpful in increasing our understanding of what really happens when loads change and control devices respond.

* * *

For a related discussion see "System Gains," in part 2 of this book.

Another factor not discussed here but present in all valves is *turn-down ratio*. This is function of valve design and quality. In any valve, in order to avoid sticking (freezing) in the closed position, there must be some clearance between plug and port. Then, as soon as the valve lifts off the seat, some minimum flow takes place. In a typical "commercial quality" valve this amounts to about 5 percent of design flow. The ratio 100:5 (percent) when reduced can be read "20 to 1"; this is the turn-down ratio.

For most HVAC applications a 20:1 ratio is satisfactory. Valves with higher ratios can be obtained if needed. On the graphs of FIGS. 5-1 and 5-5 this effect means that we should change the origin of the curves (at lower left) from zero to 5 percent of C_v or flow.

Equal percentage plugs are also known as *proportional* or *exponential*.

Pneumatic relays*

Virtually every pneumatic control system includes a relay or relays. Relays are very useful devices, allowing you to discriminate, amplify, switch, and reverse signals, among other functions. This section discusses the relay types in common use and gives some examples of their application.

In most pneumatic control systems associated with air handling systems, *electric-pneumatic* (EP) relays are used. An EP relay is simply a solenoid valve with three ports, FIG. 4-6. Control air supply is connected to the normally

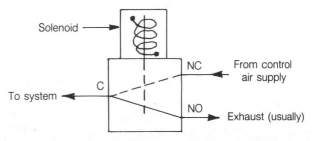

Fig. 4-6. Electric-pneumatic (EP) relay.

*July and August 1981.

closed (NC) port, and the control system is connected to the common port. The solenoid is connected in parallel with the motor starter coil or the air-handling unit fan. When the motor is running, the solenoid is energized, the valve switches to connect the NC port to the common port, and air is supplied to the controls. When the motor stops, the solenoid is de-energized, the normally open (NO) port is connected to the common port and the control system is deactivated. The EP relay can also be used in connection with individual control devices.

A PE (*pneumatic-electric*) relay performs an opposite function, opening or closing an electrical contact in response to a pneumatic signal. It is a pressure-operated electrical switch. The pressure at which contacts are opened or closed is usually adjustable. In a typical application a PE switch is controlled by outside temperature to start a preheat coil circulating pump when the outside air temperature falls below say 40°F (FIG. 4-7). The outside air sensor could serve other functions as well.

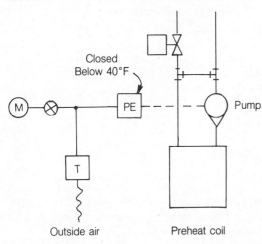

Fig. 4-7. Pneumatic-electric (PE) relay—typical application.

In the strict sense, EP and PE relays are *transducers,* since they convert one form of control energy to another. The relays discussed above are two-position or *binary* types. *Analog* types are also available, with the output signal varying in proportion to variations in the input signal. These are called I/P or P/I transducers (pneumatic-to-current or the opposite). Rarely, voltage is used rather than current. One use for a P/I transducer is the control of a variable speed fan motor in a VAV system. In FIG. 4-8 the SP sensor-controller senses static pressure and tries to maintain it at a constant value. The sensor-controller provides the control by modulating the motor speed through the P/I transducer to the speed controller.

I/P transducers are often used for setpoint reset of pneumatic local loop controls from an electronic supervisory system, FIG. 4-9.

Another frequently used relay is one that selects the higher — or lower —

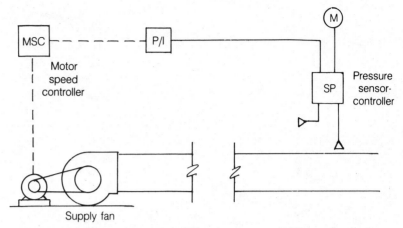

Fig. 4-8. Pressure-current (PI) transducer — VAV application.

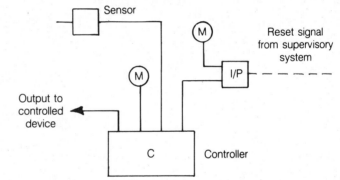

Fig. 4-9. Current-to-pressure (IP) transducer — used for reset.

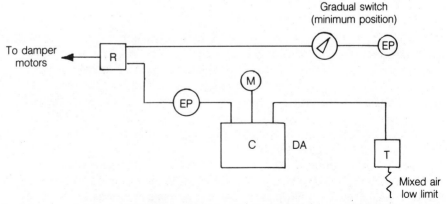

Fig. 4-10. Higher of two pressures (high select) relay — used for minimum position.

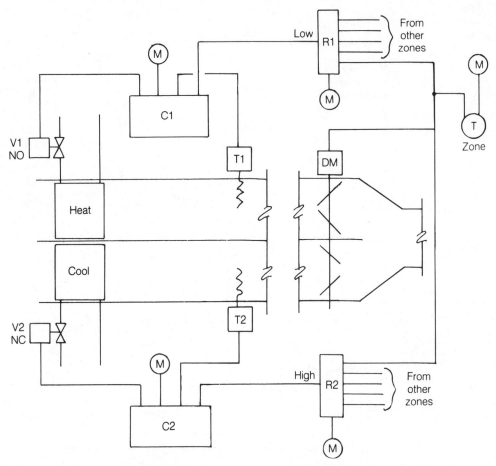

Fig. 4-11. Discriminator control — multizone unit.

of two pressures. Two signals are connected to the input ports, and the output is equal to the higher, or lower, of the input signals. A typical application of the high-pressure selector is for minimum positioning in mixed air control systems. In FIG. 4-10, the high-pressure selector inputs are the output of the mixed air temperature controller and a minimum position pressure set by a manual switch (which is simply a manually adjustable pressure regulator). Then the output of the selector is never less than the minimum regardless of the action of the mixed air controller.

An extension of the selector is the *discriminator*, which accepts a number of inputs and selects the highest or lowest (or both) for output. These relays are often used in multizone or dual-duct systems to control the hot and cold duct temperatures in the most economical manner. Figure 4-11 illustrates a typical use of both high and low selectors, utilizing zone thermostat signals in a multizone system. The selected high output is used to reset the cold-duct controller, the low output is used to reset the hot-duct controller. Although there are a great many discriminators installed in HVAC control systems, their use is subject to error. The principle sources of error are:

1. A zone thermostat set much lower or higher than others can "drive" the system to the exclusion of other signals.
2. A faulty signal can drive the system improperly. Some faulty signals are caused by human intervention.
3. The discriminator can fail to operate properly, because of age or poor maintenance, etc.

Because of these errors, many designers have looked for other methods of providing reset. The principle, however, is very good and can be used in computer-based controllers, which can be programmed to reject questionable data.

A *reversing* relay is used when the opposite value of a signal is needed. The output of a reversing relay varies from 0 to 15 pounds per square inch as the input varies from 15 to 0 pounds per square inch. A typical example of the use of this relay is control of heating and cooling coil valves from a common thermostat when it is desirable to have both valves normally closed, FIG. 4-12. Both valves are selected with an 8–13 pounds per square inch spring range; they are closed at 8 pounds per square inch and lower pressures and fully open at 13 pounds per square inch. With a reversing relay in the branch to the heating valve, the signal seen by the valves is as shown in FIG. 4-13, and the valves operate in sequence as the space temperature varies. The figure shows a deadband thermostat, but an ordinary thermostat could also be used.

An *averaging* relay is similar to a selector relay but, as the name implies, outputs the average of two to four input signals. It is used in a manner similar to that of the discriminator, recognizing that sometimes an average signal might conserve more energy than a highest or lowest signal. When averaging a group of signals, be sure that all of them are grouped over small range of temperature, humidity, or pressure.

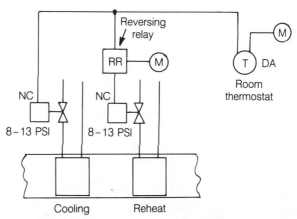

Fig. 4-12. Reversing relay-sequenced heating and cooling.

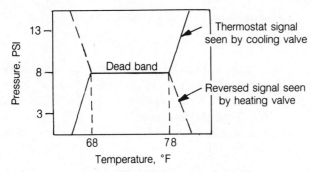

Fig. 4-13. Signal from reversing relay.

Switching relays are used extensively. A switching relay is a pneumatically operated valve, usually two-position, FIG. 4-14. Application of air pressure switches the valve from one position to the other. A spring returns it to the normal position when the pressure is removed. The spring tension determines the pressure at which switching takes place. Notice that NO and NC usage is opposite that of an electric contact relay. NO in the pneumatic relay means that port is connected to common in the de-energized position. A common use of the switching relay is for changeover to minimum outside air in an economy cycle control sequence, FIG. 4-15. Double two-position switches are used, as are three- and four-way arrangements.

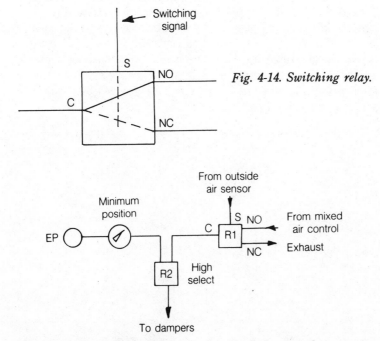

Fig. 4-14. Switching relay.

Fig. 4-15. Switching relay — mixed air control.

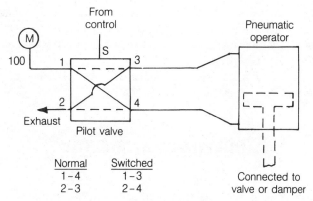

Fig. 4-16. Pilot valve relay — high-pressure operator.

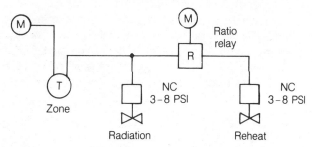

Fig. 4-17. Ratio relay — heating sequence.

A special-purpose switch is the *piloting relay*, normally used to provide high pressure air to a large valve or damper operator. Such a large operator might use 100 pounds per square inch air in a double-ended piston. The piloting valve provides air to one end or the other, as required, FIG. 4-16.

A *ratio relay* provides an output signal that is a ratio of the input signal, usually 2 to 1 or 1 to 2. It can thus provide for sequenced operation of two or more devices from a singular controller. This can also be done by varying spring ranges but sometimes the ratio relay is simpler to use. Typically, a room thermostat might control both reheat and radiation, with sequenced operation to improve comfort. In FIG. 4-17, the reheat valve is closed at a 4 pounds per square inch output signal from the room thermostat, while the radiation valve does not fully close until the setpoint (8 pounds per square inch) is reached.

This section does not exhaust the subject of pneumatic relays. There are many combinations and special-purpose relays, which your friendly neighborhood manufacturer's representative will be glad to describe to you. You now have some idea of the variety available and the uses to which pneumatic relays can be put.

* * *

This section is almost history because the trend in new control systems is toward the use of electronic or computer-based controls. Most commercial pneumatic control manufacturers feel that they will be out of the pneumatic business in 5 to 10 years. Nevertheless, there are and will remain a great many pneumatic systems in use for many more years than ten. As designers, installers, operators, and maintenance people, you need to know as much as possible about all kinds of devices.

Note that all of these relay functions are also available in electronic control devices.

Electronic controls*

Electronic controls are becoming prevalent in the HVAC industry. The growth in use of these controls is caused by a number of factors, including lower prices, improved reliability, computers, and a better understanding of electronic principles by a new generation of engineers and technicians.

It seems appropriate to discuss in general terms some of the typical electronic control equipment available today. For a discussion of how electronic controllers are constructed see reference 1 at the end of this section.

Signal levels in electronic control systems are usually 0 to 10 volts direct current or 4 to 20 milliamperes current, though other values are sometimes used.

Temperature sensors

The *platinum RTD* (resistance temperature detector) uses the principle that the resistivity of a metal is temperature dependent. The basic design utilizes a coil of fine platinum wire having a base resistance of 100 ohms at 0 degrees C (32 degrees F). *Sensitivity* (the change in resistance per unit temperature change) is low but fairly linear. This linearity and the stability of the platinum sensor over time—there is essentially no *drift*—make it the preferred sensor where accuracy and low maintenance are required. RTDs of other metals, such as nickel and nickel alloys, have higher sensitivities but not quite as good stabilities.

The low resistance of the platinum sensor means that the resistance of the *leads* (connecting wires) becomes significant. It then becomes necessary to use three or four wire leads to compensate.

On all electronic sensors, a transmitter/amplifier is required to provide a signal level appropriate to the use. This device also can provide some curve-fitting to smooth out nonlinearities.

A new type of platinum detector is the thin-film system, a development of solid-state technology. This sensor is less costly than the wound-wire type and has a base resistance of 1000 ohms or more. It also has a higher sensitivity. Because it is solid-state, it tends to drift as it ages and needs periodic recalibration.

The *thermistor* is made of *semiconductor materials* (oxides of various

*March 1986.

metals). It has a high base resistance—1000 ohms or more—and high sensitivity. It is nonlinear and requires circuitry in the transmitter to linearize the output signal. Thermistors tend to drift with time and require fairly frequent recalibration. To ensure a compatible replacement, specify factory calibrated and selected units.

Because thermistors are somewhat less costly than platinum RTDs, they are more frequently used. For long-term cost and reliability, platinum is preferable. Absolute accuracy (subject to drift) for all the sensors described is about plus or minus 0.5 degrees F. Sensitivity is 0.1 degree F or better.

Humidity sensors

Most electronic humidity sensors today use thin- or thick-film technology. A polymer film absorbs moisture until it is in balance with the ambient air. This causes a change in the sensor resistance or capacitance. This change is amplified and integrated to produce a signal for the controller. Accuracies of plus or minus 3 percent relative humidity can be specified. Because it is a solid-state device, some drift with time will occur. Drift can be specified at about one percent per year.

A better sensor is the *chilled-mirror* type. A stainless steel mirror is provided with a small thermoelectric refrigeration system. A beam of light is reflected from the mirror to a photo cell. The mirror temperature is measured by a platinum RTD. When the mirror is cooled to the dew point, condensation forms on the mirror, the change in reflected light is sensed, and the dew point temperature is read. From this and space dry-bulb temperature the instrument calculates relative humidity, or the calculation can be done by an online computer, such as a DDC. Accuracy can be specified at plus or minus 3 percent relative humidity but, in a steady-state situation, humidity can sometimes be controlled to less than one percent plus or minus. The only maintenance required is periodic cleaning of the mirror. This device is comparatively expensive but the cost may be justified by the process requirements.

Pressure sensors

Pressure sensors or pressure transducers are preferably of the piezoelectric (strain-gage) type. A solid-state semiconductor crystal is mounted on a diaphragm and deformed by changes in pressure. The deformation causes a resistance change that can be measured, linearized, and amplified to provide a signal proportional to the pressure. Good accuracies can be obtained at very low pressures—down to a few hundredths of an inch of water column.

Controllers

Electronic controllers may be modulating or two-position, as required. Modulating controllers can be used in P (proportional), I (integral), or D (derivative) modes or some combination thereof. Controllers are available with

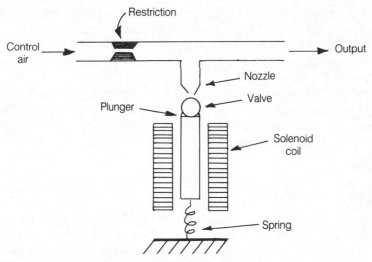

Fig. 4-18. IP (or VP) transducer.

one, two, or three inputs and up to three sequenced outputs. Controllers can also include indication of the measured value of the variable. Override switches on some instruments allow the operator to set the controller output manually. Limit alarms are also available. The electronic controller can be a very versatile instrument. Of course, all the bells and whistles increase the cost. "Plain vanilla" instruments are also obtainable.

Operators/motors

Modulating electronic operators for valves and motors can use the controller signal directly, or a transducer might be required (for example, to change from current to voltage or vice versa). Electronic operators come in a variety of sizes, configurations, and operating principles. In general they are more expensive than pneumatic operators and somewhat less reliable. Pneumatic operators require the use of current- or voltage-to-pneumatic transducers. These are of various designs, one of the simplest and best being the variable-solenoid/variable-orifice type, FIG. 4-18. The magnetic field of the solenoid coil varies with the current signal level, causing a bleed nozzle opening (and thus the pneumatic output) to vary in proportion to the controller signal.

This section is a brief and very general summary of electronic control devices. For more and better detail, consult your local control supplier or contractor. Most manufacturers are happy to provide detailed technical information and descriptions.

Reference

1. R.W. Haines, *Control Systems for Heating, Ventilating and Air Conditioning*, Fourth Edition, 1987, Van Nostrand Reinhold, pages 62–65.

Part 5

Computer-Based Control Systems

And now, at last, computer-based control systems. Remember that fundamentals do not change, and you cannot neglect fundamentals just because you have all this marvelous new technology. The new technology must be used with a full appreciation of the need for better education. Where you could get by with a limited understanding of the older, simpler control devices, the newer, sophisticated equipment is not so forgiving. It is necessary to ignore the broader claims of "all your problems will be solved" and apply your common sense and knowledge to using these new tools in the most efficient way. That advice is valid even if it means not using a computer!

The principles outlined in this section are basic and valid, regardless of technology. Some of the technology is out of date, but it is interesting to note that the basic system concept for a computer-based control system are still the same as they were before the computer. Fundamentals, again.

Interfacing an EMCS to an HVAC system*

An EMCS (energy management and control system) can be used in conjunction with an HVAC system in several ways:

1. The EMCS can be used only for monitoring with data collection and analysis. Based on the data, the HVAC system can be manually adjusted to improve performance. The data can be tabulated on a printer and can be displayed graphically in various useful ways. In this mode, the EMCS is more correctly called a *supervisory* or *monitoring* system. Many of the older systems were used for monitoring only, with some manual control functions.
2. The typical modern EMCS combines monitoring with automatic control functions of the type called *intervention* control. These functions include reset of setpoints, opening and closing of valves and dampers, and starting and stopping of motors. Except for these intervention functions, the EMCS is not involved in the local-loop controls. The local loops will continue to operate if the EMCS fails.
3. DDC (direct digital control) is the name given to the system in which the EMCS replaces the local-loop controls, and all control decisions are made by the EMCS computer. Reset of setpoints and other optimizing functions are inherent in the computer programs. This philosophy is controversial because all HVAC operations would depend entirely on the proper operation of the computer and the communication links.

It is apparent that the mode of operation desired affects the method and equipment used to interface between the EMCS and HVAC systems. Also note that EMCS equipment is almost exclusively of the low-voltage electronic type, while most HVAC controls are pneumatic and use 120 volts or higher for the electrical portions of the system.

In the monitoring mode, the EMCS is totally independent of the local-loop controls, using separate sensors for temperature, flow, pressure, and other analog functions. These sensors are, therefore, designed to be compatible with the EMCS communication system. Because all the major manufacturers use different protocols in their EMCSs, there is little or no interchangeability among these manufacturers. It is necessary to stay with the original manufacturer when modifying or adding to an existing system.

Digital monitoring includes:

1. Open/closed positions of valves and dampers, indicated by the status of limit switches on the device.

---

*May 1982.

2. Flow/no-flow status of fluids, indicated by two-position pressure or flow switches.
3. On/off status of motors, indicated by auxiliary contacts in motor starters.
4. Status of safety controls — that is, low temperature, smoke, fire — as indicated by auxiliary contacts in the devices.

Digital (two-position) devices are simply contacts which open and close and are completely interchangeable among control manufacturers.

For intervention control, both analog and digital functions are required. Resetting of a setpoint is an analog function and is usually accomplished by means of a transducer, which changes the electronic signal from the EMCS to a pneumatic analog equivalent. This signal is applied at the CPA (control point adjustment) port of the receiver-controller, FIG. 5-1.

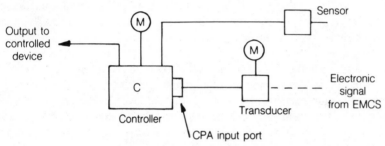

Fig. 5-1. Setpoint reset from EMCS.

Many transducers are available with various input and output characteristics. They are interchangeable so long as they match the HVAC and EMCS system requirements. An analog output can also be obtained by means of a digital signal, driving a stepping motor for some period of time. The motor could, in turn, drive a potentiometer or variable-pressure relay to provide an electrical or pneumatic signal. This procedure is not in common use.

Digital intervention controls have simply two-position signals. The EMCS signals provide a very small current and voltage and are used to drive amplifying relays with sufficient power to control even large motor starters. A wide variety of relays is available from many different manufacturers.

For direct-digital control, the entire system becomes electronic to match the EMCS. Electronic modulating operators are available for valves and dampers. This equipment is generally standardized with power requirements of 4 to 20 milliamps, 10 to 50 milliamps, or 0 to 10 volts direct current. Pneumatic operators can be used, with transducers, as noted above. Analog sensors should be electronic, compatible with the manufacturer's communication standards. Digital devices are as described above.

In 1982 most EMCS systems were used for data gathering and interven-

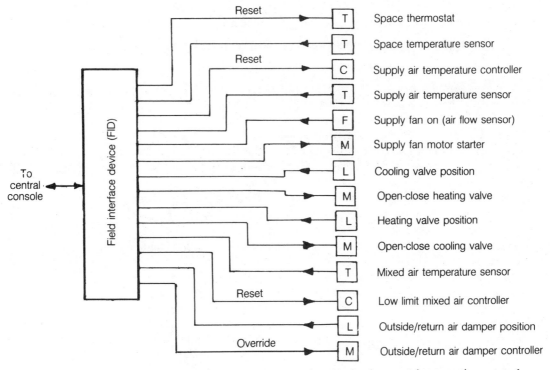

Fig. 5-2. Typical EMCS interface to HVAC system with monitoring and intervention control.

tion type control. The analog devices used were generally compatible only with one manufacturer's communication protocol and were not interchangeable. Interface to the local-loop systems was done through an FID (field-interface device), as shown in FIG. 5-2. FID is the generic term; each manufacturer has a different name for it.

The control system designer must study each project carefully and evaluate a great many conflicting claims before selecting equipment for interfacing an EMCS to an HVAC control system. It is not easy to design and specify and get a good control system.

*   *   *

This section represented the technology at the time it was written. Since then, there have been further developments, some of which are indicated in the following sections. This section is valuable, not only for history but also because the principles described have not changed, and won't. Present technology allows you to use localized, intelligent DDC for all control functions, with the EMCS serving only in a data-gathering capacity with, perhaps, some supervisory functions. It is easier now to specify a computer-based system. It still requires a high degree of skill on the part of the designer.

Monitoring and control systems: principles of operation*

One

This is the first in a series of sections that describe, in some detail, the operating principles and mechanisms used in computer-based MCS (monitoring and control systems). Although the term EMCS (energy management and control systems) is in common use, MCS is preferred because energy management is only one function of a properly designed supervisory system. Before you get into details, you need to look at some history.

Supervisory control began with the first installation of indicating or control devices at a central panel. One such system was found in an old school building. It had been installed in 1916 and consisted of a group of pneumatic switches and gauges used for positioning dampers in a forced air heating and ventilating system.

Early supervisory systems were *hard-wired*—each point was connected to the central panel by its own individual wires or tubing (FIG. 5-3). As systems became larger and more complex this method became very cumbersome. Multiplexing relays were added to reduce the number of wires required by allowing some to be used in common (FIG. 5-4). Even this simplification still required a bundle of 25 or more wires with all the related costs for installation and connection. Also, these systems were quite slow.

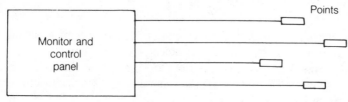

Fig. 5-3. Simple hard-wired MCS.

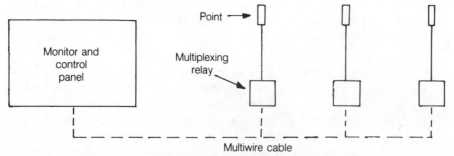

Fig. 5-4. MCS with multiplexing relays.

*August 1982–April 1983.

The advent of the computer changed all this. Because the computer can use serial transmission, the number of wires required in the primary transmission link is reduced to two—either a twisted-pair or a coaxial cable. The addition of more points as the system grows does not require any changes in the primary link. It does require other changes, which we will discuss.

Purpose   There are some misunderstandings about the purpose of supervisory control systems. Like any other machine, an MCS is simply an extension of human ideas. Its purpose is to provide data on the operating condition of systems being supervised (HVAC, lights, fire detection, security) so that proper and adequate control responses can be made. Energy conservation, better environmental conditions, and quicker reaction to alarms are byproducts of the basic functions of monitoring and control as carried out by a machine that can analyze and respond faster than a human—but still in a human way. After all, the programs the MCS uses are based on human logic and experience.

You can do all of the monitoring and control you really need without the MCS. The computer merely enables you to do these things faster and, perhaps, more efficiently. It must be applied as a tool, not as a means of solving a problem. For example, if your present HVAC systems are inefficient, the addition of an MCS will not compensate for the poor design and maintenance that created the inefficiency.

Direct functions   The direct functions of an MCS are expressed in its name. *Monitoring* means determining the status of the various points in the HVAC—or other—system. All points have either analog or binary values. The value of an analog point might vary infinitely over the range that is typical for that point—for example, temperature or pressure. A *binary* (or *digital*) point is two-position—on/off, open/closed, flow/no-flow, etc. An *alarm* is a special case of a binary point, but the monitoring system treats it the same as any other binary point. Monitoring, by itself, serves no useful purpose. It is only when the data have been received, analyzed and acted upon that any control system fulfills its function.

Control refers to a decision-making process and a resulting action. The decisions are based on the data received from the monitored points. The data are compared with criteria, such as setpoint, time, or expected status, and control commands are issued. If this sounds like a rehash of basic control theory, it is. There is nothing magic or essentially different about an MCS. When using a computer, the decision-making criteria might be more complex and sophisticated but the basic control principles remain unchanged.

Indirect functions   It is the *indirect* functions that make a computer-based MCS unique and valuable beyond an ordinary MCS. All of these functions fall under the general term of *data analysis*. They are usually given specific names, such as history, optimization, energy management, or maintenance scheduling, as discussed later.

Auxiliary functions   The computer-based MCS can also be used for other functions, such as security and fire detection. Such uses give rise to questions about reliability, speed and priorities, which do not have clear or universally accepted answers. Code problems can also arise.

Elements of the MCS   The basic elements of the computer-based MCS are shown in FIG. 5-5. The *computer* or *processor* is either a mini- or a microcomputer with an internal memory and basic operating software. It utilizes various *peripherals*, such as a *mass storage* system for storage of historical and operating data, *printers* that provide a permanent record of operating conditions, a *keyboard* for input of data and instructions by the operator, and a CRT (*cathode ray tube*) for display of systems, data and

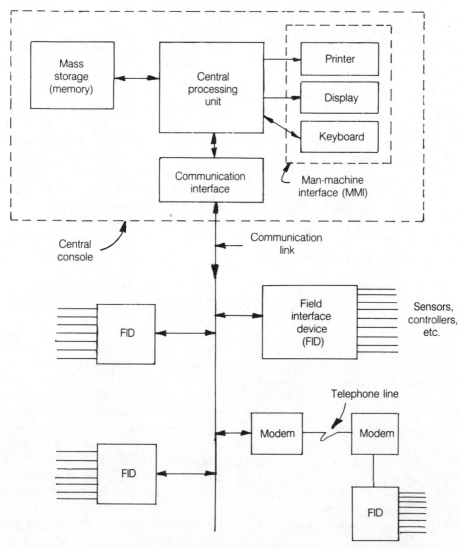

Fig. 5-5. Elements of an MCS.

operator instructions. In addition to its basic operating software, the computer uses special software designed for the MCS.

At appropriate locations near the monitored and controlled equipment there will be data collection panels, known generically as FIDs *field interface devices* (FID). Each FID serves a number of points for control or monitoring, and provides the interface between those points and the communication system.

The communication system is the link between the FID and the computer. It usually consists of a coaxial cable or a twisted pair of wires. It can also include a telephone line (with modems) for remote FID locations.

Two

In part one of this section, you find the history, purpose, and overall arrangement of monitoring and control systems. The rest of this series will deal with the specific elements of the MCS.

Begin, then, at the end—with the sensors and controllers that are the ultimate links between the MCS and the local system. *Local system* here refers to HVAC equipment, lighting or other electrical equipment, fire, security, or any other system that comes under the aegis of the MCS.

Sensors and controllers are usually referred to as *points.* It is important to understand what is and what is not a point. A point is any device that provides sensing or control of an element of the local system. Thus, temperature, pressure, and flow sensors are points, as is an auxiliary contact that indicates the status of a motor or alarm. When temperature and flow are combined to calculate Btuh, the calculation is not a true point but is sometimes referred to as a *calculated* or *implied* point, because it might have some of the characteristics of a real point. But, if a local Btu meter is provided and read by the MCS, the meter would be a point. The distinction here is between the actual sensing and control functions and the MCS calculations that precede or follow those functions.

Sensors and transmitters A *sensor* is a device that measures the present value of a variable signal. The value of an analog signal might vary infinitely with time over a range that is typical for the signal. The value of a *binary* signal is either on or off.

The most common analog signals used in HVAC work are temperature, humidity, and pressure. Flow measurement is often a function of differential pressure, though other methods are used. (For example, see "Fluid Flow Meters," by J.R. Mannion and G.A. Casedy, *Heating/Piping/Air Conditioning,* May 1982, pages 81–88). Discussion of the myriad types of sensors is beyond the scope of this book. Good sources of information are manufacturer's catalogs, *Control Engineering* magazine and *Heating/Piping/Air Conditioning* magazine. See also "Electronic Controls," in part 4 of this book.

Virtually all electronic temperature sensor transmitters use some version of the Wheatstone bridge principle. Even solid-state devices often use the principle, although their circuitry looks somewhat different.

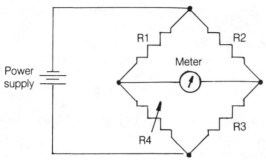

Fig. 5-6. Elementary Wheatstone bridge circuit.

Figure 5-6 shows an elementary Wheatstone bridge circuit as used for temperature sensing and indication. Resistors R1, R2, and R3 are equal. R4 is the sensor, it is often an RTD in which resistance varies as a function of temperature. As the resistance of R4 varies, the output of the meter varies proportionally and, when properly scaled, indicates temperature.

A transmitter can be substituted for the meter. The function of the transmitter is to amplify the signal and transmit it to an FID. The amplified signal is needed to overcome line losses and to minimize interference from radio-frequency noise in the vicinity of the sensor and FID. The transmitter might also provide scaling—changing the resistance signal to a voltage or current signal compatible with the FID.

The *range* of a sensor is defined by the high and low extreme values it can sense. The *span* is defined by the high and low values the point can expect to experience. The range must be greater than the span and, preferably, at least twice the span. The response of a typical temperature sensor is not linear; that is, the output signal does not vary directly with the temperature, FIG. 5-7. This error will be less significant when the span is a small part of the range.

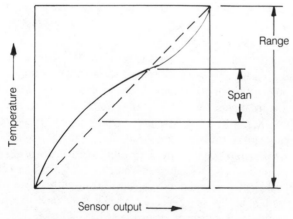

Fig. 5-7. Temperature sensor response—nonlinear.

The terms *throttling range* and *setpoint range* are sometimes used. Setpoint range is equivalent to span (a setpoint outside the span of the sensor makes no sense). Throttling range applies to pneumatic devices and is equivalent to *differential* in electric/electronic devices. It is the range of output of the controller required to drive the controlled device from one extreme to the other (for example, a valve driven from fully open to fully closed).

Some other analog values that can be sensed for use by an MCS are level (for example, of fluid in a tank), lighting level (in footcandles), power usage, and position (as of a valve or damper).

Binary sensors are two-position and usually consist of a simple contract that opens or closes to indicate a status change. Typical binary functions are: status of motors (on or off), position of valves or dampers (open or closed), and alarm and limit signals of all kinds.

For example, it might be necessary to know the position of a control valve at any point in it stroke. A sliding rheostat could provide sensing for an analog signal. In addition, limit switches could be tripped when the valve is fully open or closed, providing binary sensing. Limit switches might not be necessary because the computer could recognize certain values of the analog signal as equalling open or closed. If only the open or closed signals are needed, the analog sensor could be omitted in favor of the limit switches.

Controller   A *controller* in an MCS is the final element in the chain that delivers a control signal to the local loop. Control signals can be binary or analog. Binary (or digital) controllers are normally relays that open or close to change the status of a two-position controlled device (for example, a motor starter). Analog controllers are typically used for reset of local loop controller setpoints.

A typical reset signal from an MCS to a pneumatic receiver-controller is shown in FIG. 5-8. Here the final control element is a transducer which converts the electronic signal from the MCS to an equivalent pneumatic signal for reset of the receiver-controller setpoint. Analog controllers can also be used for direct control of valves and dampers in a direct digital control mode of operation. The local controller is eliminated. DDC operation is not normally used by the MCS. See comments at the end of this section.

The essential criterion for two-position relay section is the power capacity of its contacts. Large motor starters, for example, require several amperes for

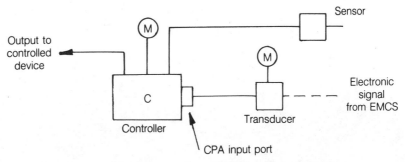

Fig. 5-8. Setpoint reset from EMCS using a transducer.

operation. For this use, heavy-duty power relays are needed and these relays are, in turn, switched by the low power capacity relays typical of the MCS.

*   *   *

Three

Field interface devices is the subject of this section. The generic name *field interface device* arises from the general function of this piece of equipment. The device is given other names by some manufacturers — *data gathering panel* is one example.

The process of interfacing between the sensors/controllers and the communication link to the CPU (central processing unit), as shown in FIG. 5-9, requires the performance of a number of operations. Early FIDs were usually

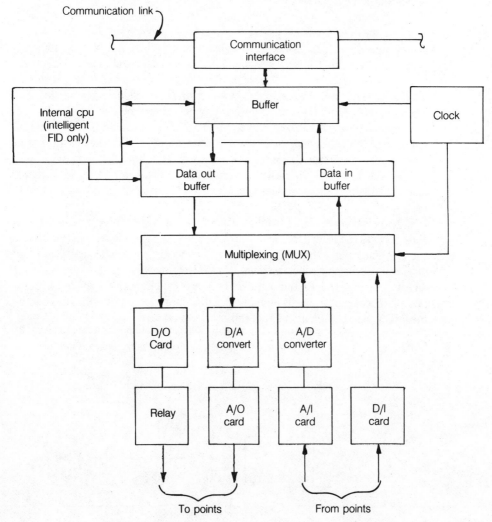

Fig. 5-9. Schematic arrangement of field-interface device.

passive, serving only as a channel of communication. The present trend is to the *intelligent* FID (IFID), which has its own computer and programs and can act in many ways as though it were a CPU. This scheme is known as *distributed processing* and has a number of advantages. The most important of these is that the intelligent FID (IFID) can operate in a stand-alone mode in case of failure of the communication link to the CPU or failure of the CPU itself.

FID functions   Functions performed by the FID include the following:

1. Receive and condition signals from analog and digital sensors (analog in = AI, digital in = DI).
2. Output analog and digital control signals (analog out = AO, digital out = DO).
3. Provide MUX (multiplexing) and timing procedures for sequencing communication with the points.
4. Provide a means of addressing and recognizing the address of each point.
5. Make calculations for the points, using scaling factors and algorithms. Convert analog values to digital equivalents (A/D) and vice versa (D/A).
6. Recognize that the value of a point has changed since the last sampling, that the value is outside of limits, or that the value represents an alarm condition.
7. Store the values temporarily and transmit them to the CPU as required.

IFIDs will, in addition, include internal programs and data for event programs and reset functions. These functions are considered in more detail in the following sections.

FID construction and operation   The typical FID is shown schematically in FIG. 5-9. The physical elements of the FID include a power supply; circuit boards (cards) for various kinds of points and also for timing, multiplexing, communication and A/D-to-D/A conversion; a card cage or rack with slots to hold the cards and a back plane for the cards to plug into; racks for power relays; terminal strips and a cabinet into which everything fits. The IFID will also include a computer.

1. Power supply: this device converts the usual 120 volts alternating current into low-voltage direct current power. The values used might vary, but are usually in the range of 12 to 24 volts direct current. For most systems, the values for analog signals fall in the range of 0 to 10 volts direct current or 0 to 50 milliamps, with 4 to 24 milliamps being the most common.
2. Point cards: each point card can handle only one or two analog points but digital cards can handle eight or more points each. Each point will have its own circuits on the card. Some systems provide a separate A/D or D/A convertor for each point, and others provide only one

(each) D/A and A/D convertor for the entire FID. Multiplexing allows each point to use the common convertor in sequence.

Digital points are easy to deal with, being simple contact closures. The card circuitry converts this into a one or zero, meaning closed or open contact, for the computer to read.

Analog points are somewhat more of a problem. Analog signals tend to deteriorate if transmitted too far. Also, an analog wire acts as an antenna to pick up electromagnetic noise from its surroundings. Thus, the analog circuit must include filters to separate the signal from the noise. In addition, all modern MCSs use digital communication, so the incoming analog signal must be converted to a digital equivalent. An outgoing signal must be converted from digital to analog. Some systems use frequency as the analog variable; this is discussed later.

3. A/D and D/A convertors: the digital communication system, like the digital computer, deals in words of, usually, 16 bits. A *bit* is a single data item with a value of one or zero. A string of bits can be used to represent a number of any value by assigning exponentially increasing values to the bits in the string as read from right to left, FIG. 5-10. Here

128	64	32	16	8	4	2	1	Value of bit
2^7	2^6	2^5	2^4	2^3	2^2	2^1	2^0	Power of two
1	0	1	0	1	0	1	0	Bit string

Fig. 5-10. Bit string representing a number.

the right-hand bit has a value of zero or one (two to the zero power). With increasing power of two the left hand bit in the eight-bit string has a value of 128 or zero. The sequence shown, 10101010, has a value of 170. If all bits are one, the eight-bit string has a value of 255. If you use this eight-bit string with an outdoor air temperature sensor with a range of 100 degrees F, you can see that the resolution is only about 0.4 degrees F. Note that with each bit you add to the string you double the resolution. That is, nine bits yields a maximum value of 511, with a resolution of 0.2 degrees F; 10 bits provides a resolution of 0.1 degrees F. This is sometimes referred to as an accuracy of 0.1 percent, but *accuracy* is not the correct word to use. For most signals in HVAC, a ten-bit convertor with another bit to indicate a plus or minus sign provides adequate resolution. Schematically, the circuitry for an analog-in point would look like FIG. 5-11.

Control output points are also divided between analog and digital types. A digital output is a relay, but the small, low-power relay on the point card cannot be used directly for control. Instead, it is used to energize a *power relay*, which is usually a sealed reed relay with adequate capacity to handle ten amps or

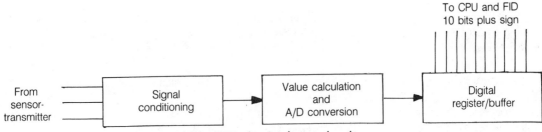

Fig. 5-11. Analog input circuit.

more and voltages up to 480 volts alternating current. The power relay can be mounted in the FID cabinet or in a separate, adjoining panel.

Analog outputs require D/A convertors, which are the reverse of A/D convertors. Eight-bit plus sign convertors are typical. The electronic analog output can be used directly if the local loop controls are electronic. For pneumatic local loops, an IP (electronic/pneumatic) transducer is required. Then the analog output circuit might look like that shown in FIG. 5-12.

Multiplexing   Because the communication link to the CPU and the internal logic of the FID must handle data in sequence, rather than simultaneously, it is necessary to organize that data and present it in sequence. This process is called multiplexing. By means of multiplexing, it is possible to talk to any specified point or to all the points in sequence. The MUX (multiplexer) has access to a list of all connected points, with their addresses. In normal operation, under the direction of a time clock, the MUX calls each point in sequence (a process known as *polling*), reads the current value, and feeds the value into a storage area known as a *buffer*. Potential alarms or critical points might be called more often than points that tend to be stable. During control changes, such as start-stop or reset, the affected points will be called more often. The calling schedule is set by the program in the MUX. If needed, the schedule can be changed, temporarily or permanently.

The data in the buffer represent the current values of the points, even though some of the data might be several seconds old. Obviously, points that are called more often will have fresher data.

Calculation and evaluation   The signal that is received from the sensor-transmitter is proportional to the real value being sensed. The FID

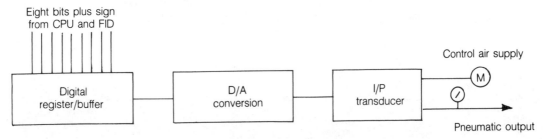

Fig. 5-12. Analog output signal to pneumatic device.

must determine the real value. An equation or algorithm, which contains the scaling constants and other functions required determines the real value. The algorithm is:

Numerical value = signal value × scaling constant ± zero base quantity

For example, if a temperature sensor transmits a signal of 10 to 50 milliamperes for a range of 0 to 100 degrees F, then 1 milliampere is equivalent to 2.5 degrees F. If the sensor is nonlinear, you would need an equation to provide a correction. The zero value would be 10 at 10 milliamperes equals 0 degrees F.

An algorithm for flow based on pressure differential would use the square root function typical of that relationship. Another calculation procedure is that of counting pulses from, for example, an electric demand meter.

The FID also compares a signal with specified high and low limits. There are two kinds of limits. One set is the normal operating limits of the point. When those limits are exceeded, something is out of control. The other set of limits is *reasonableness*. If these limits are exceeded, something is wrong with the monitoring because the point cannot reasonably take on such values. For example, a report that the chilled water temperature is 28 degrees F would hardly be reasonable.

Some operating limits are recognized as alarms. Digital alarm sensors must also be recognized. Some are alarms when open, others when closed. The FID must have the data to evaluate this. It is apparent that the FID and MCS as a whole use a great deal of data.

Communication with the CPU   Communication between the CPU and FID involves the use of digital *words*, usually 16 bits long. Each bit is either a one or a zero, with its value determined by its position in the word (see above). A typical word is shown in FIG. 5-13. The first few bits contain the address of the point. The next bits indicate the point status. Finally, one or two bits are *parity* bits for checking the accuracy of the transmission. For complex addresses or data, two or more words might be needed.

Communication validity is treated in many different ways. For example, some systems transmit everything twice, compare the transmissions, and use the data only if both transmissions are identical.

A communication interface card is used to connect to the communication link. This card provides the necessary protocol and timing to send and receive messages.

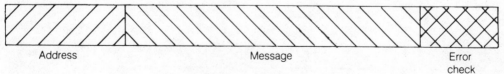

Address   Message   Error
                                                                            check

Fig. 5-13. Digital word.

Intelligent FIDs All of the above functions are performed by any standard FID. The current trend is to use intelligent FIDs (IFID), which contain small microcomputers and have some additional capabilities:

1. Change-of-state recognition. This function has been available on some systems since the beginning of computer-based MCS. It does not require a high level of intelligence. The idea is to minimize traffic on the main communication link by transmitting only change-of-state data. The FID polls all of its connected points in sequence and feeds the data into a buffer. When the points are polled the next time — a few seconds later — the data are fed into a second buffer, which is compared to the first. Only those data that have changed significantly will be transmitted to the CPU. The first buffer is then cleared and the process is repeated.
2. Event programming. One of the important functions of the MCS is the initiation of events on the basis of time or other criteria. A great deal of the event programming can be handled by the IFID, with only complex criteria being processed by the CPU. The programs will also include *constraints checks*, which are certain sequences in which events must occur or limits beyond which the HVAC systems cannot go.
3. Reset programs. Reset of setpoints is another important MCS function that can be delegated to the IFID. The CPU can furnish new criteria to the IFID from time to time, but the IFID makes the reset decisions.
4. Stand-alone mode. Because the IFID is intelligent, it can function in a stand-alone mode. That is, if the CPU or the communication link fails, the IFID can continue to supervise its connected points and provide at least some reset and event programs. The operator at the CPU console will not know what is happening, but the HVAC systems will continue to function normally.
5. Distributed processing. In addition to the higher reliability provided by stand-alone capabilities of the IFIDs, a primary objective in using them is that of minimizing traffic on the main communication link. The philosophy here is that if there is less traffic, then critical changes of state and alarms will be recognized and responded to more rapidly. The maximum *baud rate* (speed) on most digital communication systems is 4800; this means that 4800 bits per second are transmitted and processed. Over leased telephone lines and with the use of modems, speeds are often 1200 baud. In a system with 500 to 1000 points, response to any particular point could take several seconds, even when using priority interrupts. Distributed processing would avoid this.

Hardware details As in any system, the FID includes a great deal of supporting hardware to function safely and reliably. Not all of these items are included in standard packages and the methods of implementation vary. Some are necessary and all are desirable.

1. Grounding, isolation, and surge control. The system must be protected against power surges, particularly lightning. The protection is accomplished by grounding, filtering, and various isolation techniques. One of the most popular isolation methods is *optical isolation.* With optical-isolation, the low-voltage signal is transmitted from one device to another by means of a light beam, with no physical connection.
2. Indicators and switches. Most FIDs include indicators for various operational modes and for fault indication. Switches should be provided for power on/off, communication interface, and *disable*, which takes the FID out of service.
3. Backup power. Battery backup for the power supply is used for short-term power failures. The primary function of backup power is to provide an orderly shut-down with minimal loss of data. If continued operation of the MCS is critical, an emergency power source should be provided. Then the battery provides power during the period of transition to emergency power.
4. Wiring. A major part of the MCS installation cost is wiring between sensors/controllers and the FID. Any method that simplifies terminal wiring at the FID is helpful in reducing that cost. Some systems use a terminal cabinet adjacent to the FID to avoid congestion. Most systems are front-accessible. To avoid total confusion, all terminals and wiring must be clearly labeled, using nonredundant markings.
5. Expandability. The designer of the MCS should always specify expansion capability in each FID. Future point additions are typical. Each FID is designed by the manufacturer for some maximum capacity for each type of point and for total points; the original design should always be less than maximum. Use extra FIDs, if necessary, locating them to minimize the length of signal runs.
6. Cabinet. The FID is contained in a cabinet, usually built to NEMA standards. A locked door is needed, to prevent unauthorized access. The type of cabinet is dictated by the environment. An ordinary indoor environment would require only NEMA-1 (National Electrical Manufacturers' Association) construction. Outdoors might require a NEMA-12 or NEMA-4. For details of NEMA cabinets, see the NEMA standards of any manufacturer of such cabinets. An important part of the cabinet and FID design is the removal of heat generated by electrical components. Ventilation systems and heat sinks are essential to continuous, reliable operation of the system.

    Most FIDs are designed to operate satisfactorily in *normal environments*—a range of 35 to 100 degrees F and 20 to 90 percent relative humidity. The life of electronic components is increased if the environmental conditions are more moderate, particularly if they avoid the high end of temperature and humidity.

Four

The communication link between the field interface device and the central processing unit is the topic of the MCS discussion in this section.

The purpose of the communication is to allow data transmission from the FID to the CPU and commands from the CPU to the FID. Because the modern MCS uses serial transmission techniques, a single channel is sufficient for communication with a large number of points. The channel can be either a twisted pair of wires or a coaxial cable. The length of the path over which signals can be transmitted is limited by attenuation. Amplifiers can be used if needed. Transmission between buildings, even those many miles apart, uses leased telephone lines. The data to be transmitted are conditioned for voice-grade telephone lines by means of *modems.* The modem (modulator/demodulator) changes the digital or frequency signal into a signal suitable for the phone line (or vice versa). Because the speed on the phone line is often 1200 baud (bits per second) — which is less than that of the MCS — the modem also includes a buffer to store the data until they can be transmitted.

In larger systems — 500 points or more — two or more communication links can be used, each serving its own set of FIDs, FIG. 5-14. Use of more links reduces response time.

Figure 5-14 shows the relationship of the system elements. In practice, the communication link goes through the FID as shown in FIG. 5-15. Figure 5-15A shows a two-way link on which signals travel in both directions. Somewhat simpler and faster is the one way loop of FIG. 5-15B, on which all signals travel in the same direction.

Signal types used in MCS are generally digital, though frequency has been used. A digital word is usually 16 bits (FIG. 5-16) and will include the address of the point, data representing the value of the point, and one or two bit for parity and error checking. A frequency word is similar, but the values of the address and data are represented by the distance — or frequency — between the two pulses, FIG. 5-17.

In connection with the communication link, a frequently referenced standard is RS-232, "Interface between data terminal equipment and data commu-

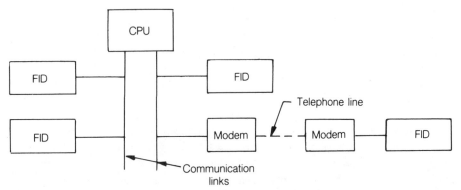

Fig. 5-14. Communication links.

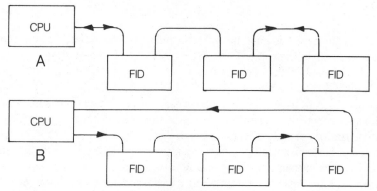

Fig. 5-15. Two-directional (A) and one-directional (B) communication links.

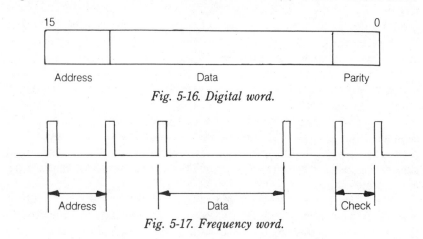

Fig. 5-16. Digital word.

Fig. 5-17. Frequency word.

nication equipment employing serial binary data interchange.'' This standard is published by the EIA (Electronic Industries Association). It establishes a standard protocol for the interface but, by itself, does not guarantee compatibility. It does make compatibility easier to obtain.

Operation   In normal operation, a continuous serial string of words is placed on the link. As each word flows through an FID, the address is checked. If the FID reads its own address, it will read the word and respond by sending data or carrying out a control command, as directed by the data portion of the word. Data will be sent to the CPU (or multiple CPUs in more complex systems). The FID can also initiate conversation by notifying the CPU that it has data to send. Traffic on the link is directed by a *traffic controller*, which is usually part of the CPU but sometimes a separate microprocessor.

Addressing   Each device in the MCS must have a unique address: each point, each FID, each CPU and all peripherals. Addressing systems vary. Some use numbers only, but most are *alphanumeric*, using combinations of letters and numbers. Often these can be combined in descriptive ways (for example, AHU1MAT equals ''Air Handling Unit 1 Mixed Air Temperature''). When the address of the point is put into the database, the address of the related FID will be included. The system software will convert the descriptive address into a digital equivalent.

Five

This section covers the central console equipment: the computer and its peripherals.

The CPU   The computer in the MCS is commonly referred to as the CPU (central processing unit). This term describes its function quite well. Here are the brains of the system, which processes the data, makes decisions, issues commands, and controls the operation of the various parts of the MCS.

The typical MCS was run by a minicomputer, but the increasing capabilities of microcomputers have allowed them to be used in many newer systems. One direction in which development is proceeding is toward the use of several microcomputers, each dedicated to a specific function within the overall system. For this discussion, assume that a single minicomputer is being used at the central console and microprocessors at the intelligent FIDs.

The functions of the CPU are as follows (FIG. 5-18):

1. The CPU drives the communication system, providing timing, addressing, checking response to FID signals and all other things necessary to ensure reliable, fast communication.
2. The data acquired from the system points are stored in the CPU. Acquired data requires *mass storage* devices — disks and tapes — and the creation of files and methods of indexing and retrieving data.
3. The data are processed by the CPU, creating the need for additional files and storage. Processing includes decision making and might result in commands issued to various elements of the MCS.
4. The CPU drives the data display devices — printers and CRTs (cathode ray tubes). The CPU decides what to display and print and when and how it should be displayed and printed.

The CPU does all this by means of *programs* which are discussed in this section. Note that the computer that runs the MCS can be, and frequently is, a state-of-the-art, off-the-shelf computer. It has to meet the requirements of the system for size and interface capability, but it need not be designed especially for use with the MCS. One of the least critical criteria for computer selection is processing speed. Even the slowest computer is still much faster than the communications link.

A very useful and desirable attribute of the CPU is *foreground-background* capability. That is, the CPU can carry on its routine activities in the *background* (invisible to the operator). At the same time, the operator can use the CPU for program development or database entry in the *foreground*. The computer should be equipped with at least one of the common assembly languages, such as BASIC. Some CPUs lack foreground-background capability

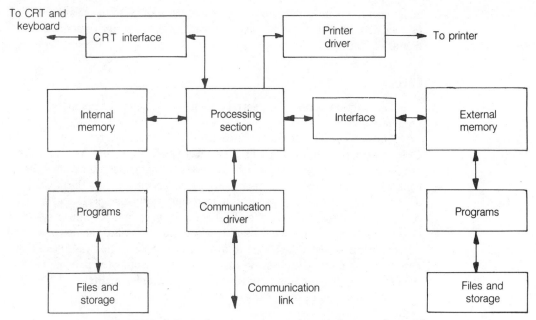

Fig. 5-18. Schematic arrangement of central processing unit.

and do not allow online programming. Then new or revised programs and data must be assembled off line (on another computer) and read into the CPU from a disk or cassette tape. The need for online programming exists only if the operator has programming capability, so offline programming might be acceptable in many situations.

Internal memories are either *volatile* or *nonvolatile*. A volatile memory is lost with loss of power and must be restored from an external source when the computer is restarted. Even with nonvolatile memory, a sudden loss of power might result in some scrambled data. Therefore, it is highly desirable to provide battery backup for the CPU for an orderly shutdown in case of power failure (or no shutdown if the failure is of short duration). An MCS that includes fire or security functions is required to have protection against power loss.

Keyboard   The keyboard is the tool through which the operator talks to the CPU, asking questions and giving instructions. The keyboard, together with the CRT and printer, is the *operator interface* with the MCS. Many articles, books, and seminars are available that cover the design of the operator interface. It should be simple, so the operator can respond quickly and confidently in a crisis, yet it must be sophisticated to avoid confusion and conflicting signals in that same crisis.

A small MCS might use a very simple keyboard, with only special function keys, but a large MCS will use a standard typewriter keyboard plus some special-function keys. There is an infinite variety of special-function keys relating to various ideas, but each has the purpose of accomplishing an often-used function with a single keystroke.

Six

Computer peripherals are discussed in this section. *Peripherals* are the various devices that relate to the CPU and, with the CPU, make up what is usually called the *central console.* The devices include CRTs (cathode ray tubes) for visual displays, printers, keyboards, and mass storage devices such as disks and tapes.

Cathode ray tube   The CRT provides the visual display to inform the operator of system status. Two types of display are used: alphanumeric (text) and graphic.

Alphanumeric displays are simply words and numbers arranged in linear or tabular form. Usually an entry will identify a point and give its status, indicating if it is normal or abnormal. Additional information about the point can be displayed: setpoint limits, maintenance status, etc. This CRT is also used for conversation between the operator and the MCS so that the operator can issue commands, ask questions, and revise programs or the database. The standard alphanumeric display consists of 25 lines of 80 characters each.

The color graphic CRT has become so sophisticated and simple to program that it has become an indispensable part of the MCS. It has superseded the slide projector displays that were typical of the older MCS designs. Using contrasting colors for clarity, it is now possible to display the HVAC systems graphically, including air-handling units, chillers, boilers, pumps, cooling towers, piping and ductwork. The display can include the identity and current value of each point and much other useful data. The technical term for this feature is *interactive display.*

All of the display can be programmed and reprogrammed from the CRT keyboard. Three or four lines of the graphic display are set aside for alphanumeric data. Because the entire screen can also be used for alphanumeric display, one CRT can serve both purposes. The typical graphic CRT has 40 lines of 80 characters each.

The slide projector mentioned above is not entirely obsolete, though it is becoming historical. It is not usually considered to be a computer peripheral, but it can be computer controlled for random or sequential slide selection, and thus looks like a peripheral.

Visual displays are called automatically or by operator command. In most systems, an alarm received by the CPU will cause a display of the system containing the point in alarm. In very sophisticated systems, instructions for dealing with the alarm can also be displayed.

The choice of visual display will be determined by the cost and degree of sophistication desired. Small systems might use a slide projector or alphanumeric display. For larger systems, it is more common to use the graphic CRT or both types of CRT together.

Printers   Printers provide a *hard copy*, a permanent, paper record of system operations and history. There are two basic types of printers and several ways of using them.

Typewriter printers have been replaced by *daisy wheel* printers (which provide print-quality records), or by dot-matrix printers (which use ink-jet techniques with a somewhat lower print quality but higher speed and more flexibility). The printer is sometimes used as a *remote terminal* with a large computer system. It is often used in a similar manner with the MCS when the operator is located somewhere other than at the central console — at a security desk, for example. The printer is used to maintain a running log of system operation, including operator inputs, points status, alarms, etc. Sometimes two units are used, with one dedicated to alarm printouts.

Line printers are high-speed devices, printing up to 300 lines per minute or even more. They are not commonly used with MCS, but have been used on occasion for large systems, primarily for summaries and historical data.

The type of printer or printers to be used depends on the basis of cost and system requirements.

Mass storage   The MCS uses much data. The computer cannot store all of this data in its rather small internal memory. Additional storage is required and is provided by disk or tape. Tape is not common in MCS, although small cassette tapes are sometimes used for inputting data and programs.

There are two types of disks:

1. The *hard disk*, so called because it is inflexible, looks like a phonograph record. The disk surface is coated with a magnetic oxide on which data can be stored electronically. In use, the disk rotates at high speed. A *fixed head*, only micro-inches above the disk surface, provides the electronic energy to *write* data onto the disk or *read* data from the disk, by induction (FIG. 5-19). Software provides instructions for addressing, storing, and retrieving the data. A hard disk can store several million bits of data (capacity is usually expressed in *megabytes*). Retrieval time — the time required by the CPU to call for a data item, read it, and store it in the CPU memory — is typically on the order of a few microseconds or less.

2. The *floppy disk* is a smaller, thin, flexible disk used extensively with microprocessor systems. Because they are small and thin, these disks are cheap and easy to file away for permanent storage of data. They operate on the same principles as the hard disk but have much smaller capacity per disk. Small systems generally use the floppy disk, and large systems might use both types.

Operator interface   The keyboard, the CRT displays, and the printer are the operator interface with the system. The proper design of the interface will keep the operator informed and involved in the system operation and will avoiding confusion in the presentation of data and alarms. There are many theories and procedures in this area, and the would-be designer should make a careful study of the subject of person-machine interface.

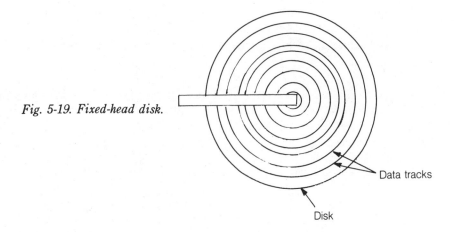

Fig. 5-19. Fixed-head disk.

Data tracks

Disk

Seven

Software—or programming—is necessary to make the computer operate. Some programs are made a permanent part of the CPU when it is constructed. This type of software is sometimes called *firmware* because it cannot be erased. To the system user, it looks like part of the hardware. The programs used for MCS operation are input to the CPU by compiling in either *machine language* or an *assembler language.* All modern computers use some kind of assembler language, such as FORTRAN, BASIC, COBOL, or others. Many MCS systems use a special language that is peculiar to that system. Some of the older systems had no online compilation capability. Programs and database had to be compiled off line (on another computer) and input to the CPU by cassette tape or floppy disk. The assembler language is itself a program and part of the overall system software.

Software classifications   Software can be grouped into four general classifications. The actual groupings and terms vary from one manufacturer to another, and these descriptions are generic.

1. *Executive software* is that required to make the computer operate. It might be called the elementary education of the computer. It allows the computer to start up when turned on or after a power failure. The startup is called *boot strapping.* Executive software covers all of the basic operations of the computer, including the ability to read the machine language, by which additional programs are entered. It should also include calculating ability and internal test and diagnostic programs.

2. *Operating software* is the higher education of the computer. This software includes the capability of doing several things simultaneously, which is called *multitasking.* Actually, operations are not simultaneous but, by means of a method called *time sharing,* several operations can go on essentially simultaneously. Operating software can also include file management—procedures for developing and locating

storage spaces for data in the various storage areas that are available; *queueing*—the ability to hold one or more operations in abeyance until a present task is complete; control of peripherals; and restart procedures.

3. *Program development software* allows new programs to be developed online and includes assembler languages. On some older systems, online development was not available.

4. *Application software* includes the special programs used by the MCS for entering, reading, and interpreting data; calculating capacities and efficiencies; making decisions, such as reset of setpoints, maintenance scheduling; and all the other good things the MCS can do to improve system operation and save energy. Most MCS manufacturers have a list of standard software packages available for the most often used analyses and procedures.

Intelligent FID programs   It has been noted that the IFID can include programs for some of the simpler, routine supervisory operations. The capability of the IFID is limited by its internal memory.

Database   Every MCS requires a database. The database is a list of all the points in the system, with file addresses, names, and information about the point. The information can include a number of elements, as shown in TABLE 5-1. The database can also include all of the desired HVAC maintenance instructions, together with the criteria for each message to be displayed and printed. The computer needs a program for inputting new or revised information into the database. Currently such programs are interactive, providing a series of questions to be answered by the operator. When all questions have been answered and the data entered, the new database entry is usable. The programs check data to avoid redundant file names and addresses.

Application program writing   There are standard application software packages that are tested and proved each manufacturer for its particular hardware. These packages should be used whenever possible. Sometimes a special program is needed. Most HVAC design engineers do not have the

Table 5-1. Board/Port/Channel Schedule

Point Acronym	Point Number	Point Type	Board	Port	Channel
AH01SASF	211	DO	1	1	3
AH01OADM	202	DO	1	1	4
AH01TSOA	201	AI	2	-	2
AH01PFDP	203	AI	2	-	3
AH01TSRA	205	AI	2	-	4
AH01TSMA	206	AI	2	-	5
AH01CCVV	207	AO	3	-	0
AH01HMVV	217	AO	3	-	3
AH01TSZN	222	AI	4	-	13

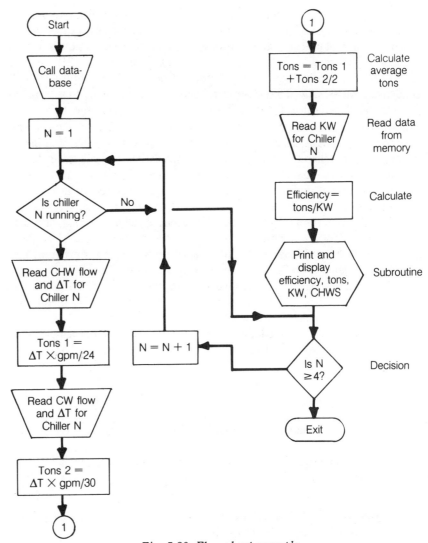

Fig. 5-20. Flow chart example.

programming expertise to write the detailed program. If you wish to try it, get the computer manufacturer's instruction book and a good text on the specific assembler language used by the computer. An experienced programmer can provide the detailed *coding* (programs) if you provide a *flow chart* outlining the program logic.

To make a flow chart, develop a step-by-step logical procedure, just as you would do it manually, but remember that the computer must make all decisions in terms of yes or no. This method of thinking is sometimes difficult for a designer, who is accustomed to making judgements based on experience. After developing the logical procedure, express the procedure in standard flow chart symbols, as illustrated in the following example.

Assume you have a central chiller plant with four chillers driven by electric motors. You wish to express the efficiency of each chiller as the ratio of tons output per kilowatt input. The ratio is not true efficiency, but it is a good measure of performance. You can calculate tons as a function of CHW (chilled water) flow rate and temperature difference from supply to return, or CW (condensing water) flow and temperature difference from supply to return. To improve accuracy, calculates tons both ways and average the two. Read kilowatts from a meter on the motor. Make a flow chart (FIG. 5-20) showing the necessary steps in the calculation. By setting N equal to one first and incrementing it by one each time you perform the calculation, you will calculate the efficiency of each of the four chillers in sequence. If a chiller is not running, skip that calculation and go on to the next chiller. The value of 30 in the tons calculation for CW is based on 15,000 Btuh heat rejection per ton, but it might be slightly different for a specific chiller. The steps of calling, reading, printing, and displaying data are *subroutines*, involving many more steps. This whole program is itself a subroutine, which is called up by the main program line whenever efficiency is to be calculated, usually on a time basis.

When many decisions involving several parameters are to be made, the flow chart can become very complex and difficult to follow. It is useful, and even necessary, to include explanatory notes with some steps.

The process just described is called *system analysis*. It can be simple, as in this analysis, or complex. It always requires that the systems analyst possess three attributes:

1. An understanding of the principles of programming and computer operation.
2. The ability to analyze and organize a problem into a logical sequence and solution.
3. A thorough understanding of the system (for example, an HVAC system) being dealt with.

Summary   These discussions of computer-based monitoring and control systems is not exhaustive. For those interested in further study:

1. Technical data sheets of MCS and DDC manufacturers are useful for comparing capabilities.
2. The *ASHRAE Proceedings* include many papers on MCS-related topics.
3. The *ASHRAE Journal* and *Heating/Piping/Air Conditioning* magazine publish many articles in this area.
4. Also see the next section.

* * *

You might have noticed that some of the technology described in these discussions on MCS is a bit out of date. The fundamental principles and logic remain unchanged. There are technological changes that have taken place and are still taking place.

A major change has been the emergence of the PC (personal computer) as a flexible, powerful device. Combined with standard interface modules, which provide the needed signal conditioning and conversion, these PCs can do any and all of the computer operations required. The present trend is to a completely *distributed* system, using PCs or specially designed DDCs for direct digital control and allowing the PCs or DDCs to use a common communication network to talk to one another. If a central console is desired, another PC can be dedicated to run it. The new computers (but not the special DDCs) also include, as standard options, large-capacity hard disk memories as well as floppy disks. The new DDCs and PCs, when used as DDCs, act exactly like IFIDs, except that they are much more powerful. So FIDs are no longer necessary.

These systems include a large amount of *packaged* (furnished with the system) software, including interactive software to simplify the task of inputting or changing the database. Custom software can still be provided, but things are much simpler than they used to be.

The communication links at the local level are almost entirely twisted pairs. At the PC-to-PC level, twisted pairs are also used, but optical fiber will be the norm in the near future. The use of optical fiber for phone lines will speed up communications, at a time when the need for speed has decreased because of distributed processing. There is more than one solution to a problem!

There are now automatic dial-up modems, which practically eliminate the need for leased telephone lines.

Special keyboards are essentially passe, except on some small, special-purpose DDCs. The standard PC keyboard has all the flexibility needed.

The laser printer is the newest development in computer printing. Laser printers are fast and have the capability of producing a large number of different type fonts as well as graphic prints. This flexibility makes them very useful.

All of this is as of now. In a short time, the technology might take several more giant strides. Just don't forget the history and the fundamentals.

Defining MCS requirements*

Components and workings of MCS (monitoring and control systems) have been discussed previously. However, the understanding of how the system works and the determination of how it is to be used in a specific installation are two different things.

The first problem arises from system capability. Given the proper sensors, controllers, and software, the system can do almost anything (including talk). Faced with this smorgasbord of goodies, you can get quite excited — until you read the prices on the menu.

---

*May 1983.

Getting back to reality, how do you define the real requirements of a specific MCS? What criteria do you use? First, you must assume that existing HVAC and other energy consuming systems (for example, lighting) have been studied, upgraded, and retrofit to work in the most efficient manner possible. Then, you must assume that a cost analysis has been made to show that an MCS can be justified on the basis of energy and other cost savings. On these bases, you sometimes can make a decision to use an MCS. Now you can talk about specifics.

General criteria

At a workshop sponsored by NIBS (National Institute of Building Sciences), the group developed a list of seven general criteria or questions to be answered:

1. How is the building used?
2. What is the size, capability, and utilization of the existing maintenance and operation staff?
3. What MCS control strategies are available and what results can be expected from each?
4. What are the budgetary restraints?
5. What are the personnel restraints?
6. Are there any constraints regarding interruptions of existing operations or related programs?
7. What about flexibility and expandability, now and in the future?

These questions are discussed in more detail in the following paragraphs.

How is the building used?   Here you need to define the comfort or process requirements, the hours of occupancy, the types of HVAC and electrical systems installed, and any special or unusual requirements. From this, you can determine operating schedules and load-shedding possibilities and define the limits to be observed in maintaining a required environment. For example, exhaust fans in a laboratory or a hospital cannot be cycled nor can the amount of outside air required to make up that exhaust be limited.

Maintenance and operation staff   Staff might be a large and well-trained group for an industrial facility or it might be a janitor who has been shown how to start and stop the equipment. Can this staff be trained to use the MCS, or will additional personnel be required? If added people are necessary, how can they be obtained and budgeted for? Can an outside service organization be used for maintenance? How are the operating people to be trained? It is a fact that the MCS will not work as it should—and sometimes not at all—if the operating staff is not properly trained and motivated.

What is available?   As noted at the beginning of this section, everything is available—well, almost everything. Specific answers can be obtained from the equipment suppliers. Standard modules of hardware and software are usually cheaper and, having been tested, cause fewer problems than custom software and special hardware configurations. Most systems will require some custom software. The best design, from economic and operating standpoints, will have the fewest custom requirements.

Budget restraints   There are always restraints. Probably a budget was developed when the decision was made to use an MCS. So, if more functions are requested than can be purchased, some priorities must be established. Remote terminals and printers are nice to have but are they really necessary? The basic console and communication system can usually accommodate a wide range of points, and there is a tendency to feel that added points cost little or nothing. Although incremental cost might appear small in comparison to total system cost, each point must be carefully evaluated for need and use, or the cost will soon be out of control. System size also has an effect on maintenance costs. Have these been properly budgeted for?

Personnel restraints   These restraints are partially covered above. The workshop discussions highlighted the fact that personnel with special skills are required for MCS system maintenance. Use of an MCS might increase, rather than decrease, the size of the operating and maintenance staff. In any case, it will change the mix of skills required.

Interruption of existing operations   Installation of an MCS can create some equipment shutdown requirements. For example, installation of temperature, flow, and pressure sensors in chillers will require the shutdown of at least one chiller at a time. If this will cause an unacceptable shutdown on the building operation, then creative alternatives must be explored. (Can this piping be hot tapped? Is the point really needed?) To avoid equipment failures, the MCS must be complete and carefully tested before it is put on line.

Flexibility and expansion   *Flexibility* is the capability of revising programs, database and other software in simple ways, preferably on line and without the use of highly skilled programmers. There is a wide variation in this capability among the available systems.

Expansion simply means that one point or 1000 points, or additional computers, consoles, printers, etc., can be added to the system. The principal question is cost. Most systems are designed and installed with spare capacity. The addition of points then requires no change in hardware beyond that required for the point itself. When the limit of spare capacity is reached, some major changes might be necessary, and the cost per point will increase. In other systems the addition of points might be possible but only with a decrease in system response time — which might not be acceptable.

Conclusion   The points to be recognized in connection with the purchase of an MCS are these:

1. It is not magic. It will not clear up operating problems in the present HVAC system or other systems. These must be dealt with before the MCS is applied.
2. Careful consideration must be given to the objectives and purposes of using the MCS in a particular installation.
3. An MCS is a system. It must be treated as such and not as an isolated device that is tacked on to the existing systems.

4. An MCS is a tool to be used to improve the operation of the HVAC system and other systems. Like any tool, it can be used correctly, incorrectly, or not at all.

DDC (direct-digital control)*

A prominent buzz word in the HVAC control industry is *DDC* (direct-digital control). At a seminar during the June 1983, ASHRAE annual meeting on the subject "Interfacing EMCS to Local Loop Controls," five papers were presented. Three were on DDC. HPAC (*Heating, Piping, and Air Conditioning*) and the *ASHRAE Journal* are full of advertisements for DDC equipment. Just what is DDC, anyhow?

DDC is something like a religion in that there is general agreement on a few common points and a wide variety of opinions on details. In this discussion, DDC is defined in terms of the commonly accepted functions, and some of the variable features are described.

A DDC is a microprocessor-based unit designed to be used for local loop HVAC (or other) control. It can interface directly with the local-loop sensors and controlled devices, replacing the usual local-loop controllers and many of the relay and switching functions. The computer can be programmed for normal operation of the HVAC system plus most of the energy conserving functions normally associated with a large central computer. The number of points served by a single DDC and its internal programming is limited by its internal memory. Still, the DDC is much more powerful and provides much better control than the typical "dumb" local-loop controller.

All DDC units are designed to function on a stand-alone basis. That is, they can operate satisfactorily without connection to a central computer. If a central computer (CPU) is added and connected to the DDC; then the DDC can function like an intelligent FID. In this mode, the CPU can change the DDC programs and database, and it can provide overall optimization.

Input/output capacity of the DDC varies from one manufacturer to another. All units provide for both analog and digital input/output, AI, DI, AO, DO (see Fig. 5-21). Through the use of transducers, all systems can interface with pneumatic sensors and controlled devices.

Programming is accomplished in several ways. Many special units can be programmed by means of a PPU (portable programming unit), which can be plugged into the DDC temporarily. The PPU includes a keyboard and simple display and is used to enter or alter programs and to read the status of the DDC. Programs can also be compiled off line by the PPU or a master CPU and put on cassette tape, which can then be read by the DDC. If the DDC is part of

---

*September 1983.

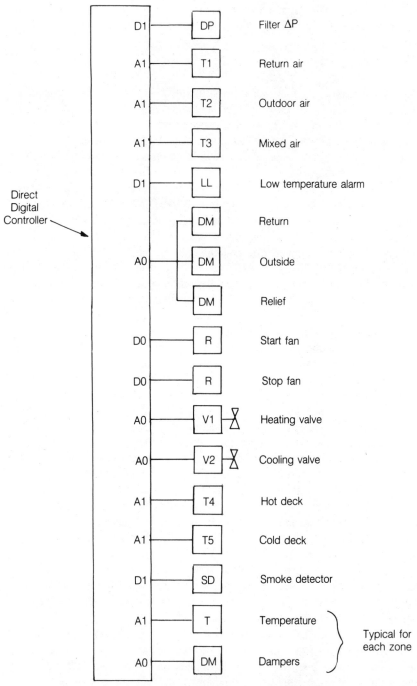

Fig. 5-21. DDC interface to a multizone unit.

an overall system with connection to a CPU, then programs can be down loaded directly from the CPU. (Most modern DDCs include programming capability.)

Programming languages for special DDCs are usually special. For DDCs designed to interface with a larger MCS, the language used is that of the MCS. (Standard process control or personal computers used for DDC include a standard programming language.) Most languages are deliberately simple to make the DDC easy to use. All require some study, and the operator will go through a learning process before becoming skilled in the language.

Not all DDC units include display of data or operating status. The PPU always includes a display and can be plugged into the DDC temporarily or permanently to read data. Most DDC units can be connected to a common *bus* (communication link). In some systems, one of the DDC units can be used to interface with a CRT or printer to read-and-record data from the other DDCs. In other systems, the PPU or an operations terminal can be permanently connected and used for monitoring and changing programs.

Connection of the DDC unit to a larger MCS with a CPU depends, to some extent, on the compatibility of the two elements. Most of the major HVAC control manufacturers provide compatibility between their own DDC units and CPUs. However, the problem of inter-manufacturer compatibility is still present. Most DDC units are designed to interface with electronic control devices at 4 to 20 milliamperes or 0 to 10 volts direct current. They are quite compatible at this hardware level. Software is still a problem because protocol, message structure, and language vary greatly among manufacturers. Mixing and matching system elements is not simple.

A desirable element in any DDC is a battery backup for preserving the memory on power failure. Backup capabilities vary from simple power-down preservation of memory to continuing operation for several hours. Some MCS designers consider direct control of the local loop from the CPU to be direct digital control. In a sense this is true, but there are some important comparisons to be made with local-loop DDC. The first is reliability. The CPU and its communication system have a greater potential for failure than a local loop DDC. CPU failure affects all the systems in the building, but local DDC failure affects only one or two systems. Therefore, with CPU control, an ordinary local-loop control system must be provided as a backup. Second is communication speed. In a large system (500 or more points) it might take several minutes for the CPU to read all sensor points and take appropriate action. Then control response might be inadequate to provide the required environment. A local DDC is able to respond very quickly.

An advantage of DDC is the use of PI (proportional-plus-integral) control mode, in lieu of the usual simple (proportional) control of commercial controllers. This results in more accurate control, as shown in FIGs. 5-22 and 5-23, because "offset" is inherent with proportional control but is virtually eliminated with PI control. *Offset* is the difference between the setpoint and the actual value of the controlled variable under dynamic loading conditions.

It is possible to utilize a standard programmable process controller or a personal computer as a DDC. Many makes of these devices are available; some

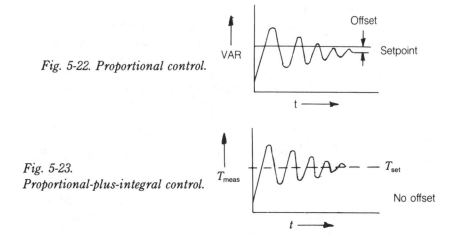

Fig. 5-22. Proportional control.

Fig. 5-23.
Proportional-plus-integral control.

of them are extremely simple to install and operate. All have user-friendly software, and programs are developed using simple control logic. Interface to a CPU is also possible, although intervention control from the CPU causes some software problems.

The decreasing cost of the microcomputer and electronic components in general is making the DDC approach more desirable and more economical. Some version of DDC will be the typical HVAC control system within the next decade.

* * *

Predicting that DDC will be the typical HVAC control system within the next decade is not difficult. The growth of DDC is continuing. There are many special DDC units available, with firmware for specific functions such as controlling a VAV box. The use of PCs for general-purpose DDC is also growing. There are still the problems of training and maintenance to be solved on large scale, but computer knowledge and acceptance by more people should help in this area. The cost of DDC control has decreased dramatically to the point where it is tempting to buy too much. I still believe that DDC will be the way to go in the foreseeable future.

Software for a
direct-digital controller*

One of the options available to the owner/operator of a DDC system is that of writing software. Two factors are making it easier to exercise this option: DDCs are becoming easier to program, and more people, including owners and operators, are acquiring and using personal computers.

Many of the DDCs now available are essentially personal computers with

*May, July, and August 1985.

the added capability of interfacing with the outside world for acquiring data and issuing commands. They can be programmed in BASIC or some similar language. Thus, if the DDC is properly selected, anyone who understands the principles of programming can quickly learn to write the software to control the related HVAC systems and equipment.

This section describes the procedures required to prepare the system and develop the software. You, too, can be a systems analyst!

Preparation for software begins with the design of the control system. This step is needed no matter who is to write the programs. Three things are required: schematic drawings, control sequences, and an IO (input/output) schedule.

Schematic drawings should be generic, similar to FIG. 5-24. This schematic is drawn for a DDC: only sensors and controlled devices are shown. All of the control logic will be in the DDC software. The point numbers shown on the DDC interfaces are important. They will show up later on the electrical schematic and the I/O list. They can and should also be used as wiring labels and on control submittals. The consistent use of the same numbers throughout the project makes coordination and commissioning much simpler.

The electrical schematic, FIG. 5-25, shows the interfaces between the DDC and the fan motor starter control and status circuits. Some systems might also include variable-speed control, open/close control for valves and dampers, and other similar functions.

The *sequence of operation*, FIG. 5-26, is a written description of how the control system is to function. It might also be called a control strategy. The description is needed because not all control strategies are self-evident from the schematic diagrams.

The I/O schedule, FIG. 5-27, is derived from the schematics and the sequence of operation. Some functions are added to those shown on the schematic. These include display and log—where a CRT and printer are available—and alarm functions. Alarms can be *critical, off-normal* or *maintenance*. Critical alarms indicate an unsafe or shutdown condition. Off-normal indicates that the process is out of control but still functioning. Maintenance alarms indicate that maintenance is to be performed, based on calendar or run time. If there is a CRT with graphic capabilities, a system schematic might be displayed. This is common for large systems but not for DDC. The same numbers that are used in the schematic are also used in the I/O schedule.

Sensors and actuators

It is preferable to use electronic sensors for DDC systems because they can be interfaced directly. Most electronic analog sensors can now be obtained with a 4 to 20 milliampere signal, though others, such as 10 to 50 milliamperes or 0 to 10 volts direct current might be encountered. For a 4 to 20 milliampere signal range, if the temperature sensor has a nominal range of 40 to 140 degrees F, a signal level of 4 milliamperes is equivalent to a 40 degree F temperature and a signal level of 20 is equivalent to 140 degrees F. Intermediate temperatures are proportional to the intermediate signal levels. Signal

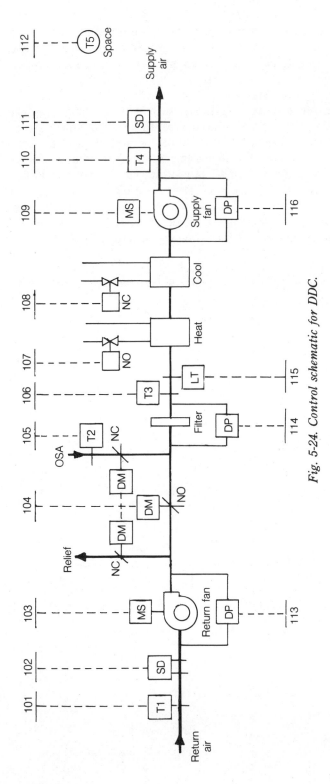

Fig. 5-24. Control schematic for DDC.

levels above 20 and below 4 milliamperes are translated in the same proportionate scale. Because the computer makes a very accurate linear interpolation — or extrapolation — the accuracy of the temperature value obtained depends on the linearity of the sensor, as corrected by its transmitter. So the sensor-transmitter must be specified to be linear within a small error.

Actuators for valves and dampers can be electronic or pneumatic. Pneumatic actuators with positive positioners work well, but there are many occasions when an electronic device might be desirable. Because the analog output of the DDC is usually a 4 to 20 milliampere signal, transducers are required for pneumatic actuators. A number of good transducers are now available. Good linearity is the principle criterion. The typical I/P (current-to-pressure) transducer provides a 3 to 15 pounds per square inch output in response to a 4 to 20 milliampere input. Transducers for other input signals, such as 10 to 50 milliampere, are available but must be specified since they cannot be altered in the field.

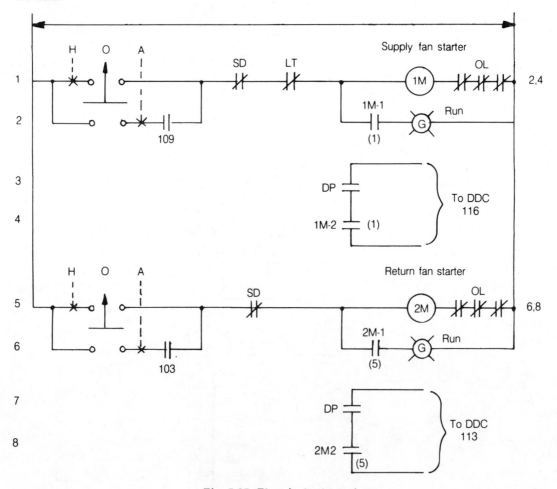

Fig. 5-25. Electrical schematic.

The DDC

In simplifying the writing of programs, not all DDCs are equal. Many systems still require you to learn a special language or even to program off line — on a larger computer — and download the program to the DDC. The trend is toward the use of some standard language, such as BASIC, which is

---

SEQUENCE OF OPERATION

1. The supply and return fans are started and stopped on a time schedule. Manual override is provided. The supply air smoke detector or the low temperature safety switch will stop the supply fan if tripped. The return air smoke detector will stop the return fan if tripped. In either case the DDC will stop the other fan. Fan status is determined by means of auxiliary contacts in the motor starters and by pressure differential switches. When the fan fails to start as commanded, an alarm signal is provided.

2. The outside, return air and relief dampers are controlled on "economy cycle" as follows:
   a. When the supply fan is "off" the outside and relief air dampers are closed and the return damper is open.
   b. When the supply fan is "on" the outside air damper opens to a minimum position as required for ventilation and is further controlled as described below. Relief and return dampers "track" the outside air damper: relief damper opens and return damper closes as the outside damper opens.
   c. If the outside air temperature (T2) is below 55°F, the dampers are positioned to provide a mixed air temperature as measured by T3 and determined by the space temperature (T5) in accordance with the following schedule:

Space temperature	Mixed air temperature
78°F	56°F
70°F	70°F

   d. If the outside air temperature is between 55°F and 70°F, outside and relief dampers are fully open and return damper is closed.
   e. If the outside air temperature is between 70°F and 80°F, then return air (T1) and outside air temperatures are compared. If return air temperature is higher than outside air temperature, 100 percent outside air is used as described in d. above. If the return air temperature is lower, then the outside damper goes to minimum as described in b. above.
   f. If the outside air temperature is above 80°F, the outside damper is in minimum position as described in b. above.

3. Heating and cooling coil valves are modulated to provide heating or cooling to satisfy the space requirements. The valves are sequenced so that heating and cooling are not provided simultaneously. The supply air temperature is adjusted in accordance with the following schedule:

Space temperature	Supply air temperature
78°F	56°F
70°F	70°F

Fig. 5-26. DDC sequence of operation.

relatively simple to learn and use, particularly for those users who are acquainted with personal computers in the home or office. Some of the most usable DDCs come to HVAC from the process control field, where they are known as *programmable process controllers*. Some of these are programmed using Boolean algebra logic systems rather than conventional programming languages. This approach is not well suited to analog users.

The DDC interface must accommodate four types of signals:

1. DI (digital in), an open or closed contact, denoting a status or alarm condition.
2. DO (digital out), a two-position control output (relay) that can be used to open or close a valve or damper or start or stop a motor.
3. AI (analog in), a signal from an analog sensor-transmitter.
4. AO (analog out), an analog output signal to drive a damper or valve actuator or vary the speed of a motor.

Figure 5-28 shows the DDC interface requirements for the HVAC system shown in FIG. 5-24. The power relays for fan motor start/stop are not a part of the DDC proper but are driven by smaller relays in the DDC. The relays in the DDC will not normally provide enough power to energize a motor starter coil. Some relay outputs are momentary contact. Some DDCs provide a timed-pulse

Job No. _____ Page No. _____ Issue Date _____ Revised Date _____	Analog Indication					Binary Indication			Command				Log		Alarm		
	Temperature	Humidity	Diff. Pressure			On-Off	Flow-No Flow	Diff. Pressure	Start-Stop	Open-Close	Modulate	Display	Regular	Maintenance	Critical	Off-Normal	Maintenance
AHU No. 1																	
Return air 101	X												X				
Return air smoke detector 102						X							X		X		
Return fan 103 113						X	X		X				X	X	X		
Return, relief, OSA dampers 104											X		X				
Outside air 105	X												X				
Mixed air 106	X												X				
Heating coil valve 107											X						
Cooling coil valve 108											X						
Supply fan 109 116						X	X		X				X				
Supply air 110	X												X				
Supply smoke detector 111						X							X		X		
Space 112	X												X			X	
Filter 114								X						X			X
Low temperature safety 115						X							X		X		

Fig. 5-27. I/O summary.

output in lieu of the conventional analog signal. Timed-pulse output requires a special type of transducer using a stepping motor.

Because there is such a wide variety of DDC capabilities available, it is very important to write a DDC specification that meets the needs of the user and can be interfaced with the HVAC system in a manner suitable to the user's requirements for both hardware and software. The specification takes some time, study, and effort on the part of the designer, but it pays off in flexibility and ease of operation.

Now consider how the programs are developed. The production of any software program includes several steps:

1. Planning, outline, and analysis.
2. Coding (writing the program).
3. Testing and debugging.
4. Installing, and testing in operation.
5. Adjustment and tuning for best performance.

Planning

Planning the program is sometimes called system analysis. Based on the information furnished by the HVAC system designer, an outline of the control sequence is developed. Additional information might be needed and must be

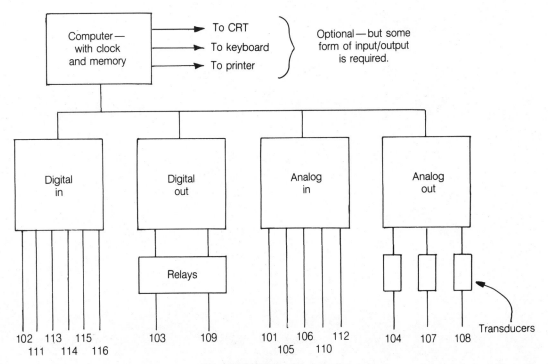

Fig. 5-28. DDC with interface.

obtained at this stage. For example, if the supply fan is to be started and stopped on a time sequence, the times to be used must be established. For analog controls, the setpoints, limits, and algorithms must be determined. Similar information is needed for all points relating to the DDC.

Programs are preferably written as *subroutines* or *modules*. Each of these small elements deals with a specific operation, such as start/stop of a fan. The modules are then strung together by a *main line* program that deals with the total sequence. Modification to a module has no effect on the mainline sequence. A flow chart is the commonly used method of outlining a program. The flow chart shows all of the major steps and decisions needed in the program. Figure 5-29 is a flow chart for a subroutine to start/stop a fan on a time schedule. The decision-making process is indicated by the diamond-shaped enclosure with two branches. The computer is limited to yes-no decisions. Similar flow charts can be constructed for all the elements of the program.

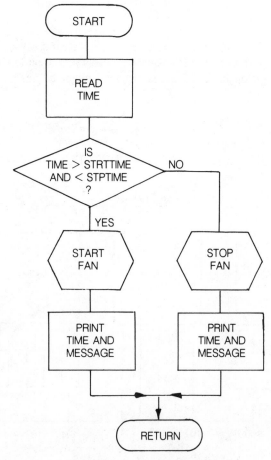

Fig. 5-29. Program flow chart.

Reading or outputting data from and to the various point requires that each point name be established and the channel or port on the DDC board to which the point is connected by identified (TABLE 5-1). The program must define these things and add a step that interprets an incoming signal level as a value of temperature, humidity, pressure, etc. The interpretation requires an algorithm that includes the relationship between the signal level and the value of the variable defined thereby, including the base or *zero* level. *Scale* and *range* might be more meaningful terms to some readers.

The points should be defined as *real* (analog) or *integer* variables and given a descriptive acronym. A typical acronym for the start/stop supply fan digital output would be AH01SASF.

For analog control, an algorithm is required. For DDC control of HVAC, PI control is recommended. (See reference 1 at the end of this section.) The equation for PI control is:

$$Q = A + K_p e + K_i \int e \, dt \qquad (5\text{-}1)$$

where: Q = control output
A = a constant equal to control output when e is zero
K_p = Proportional gain
K_i = Integral gain
e = error signal, the difference between the measured value of the controlled variable and the setpoint

In the DDC, integration can be accomplished using Simpson's Rule. The error is multiplied by the time interval (between readings), and this product is stored and used for output. At the next time interval, the new product is added to the stored value, and the sum is used in calculating output. The sum continues to increase until the error signal changes sign or some maximum output signal is reached.

For direct-acting control, the error is calculated as the measured value minus the setpoint. For reverse-acting control, the opposite is true.

The time interval is determined by the time required for the DDC to scan all of its connected points and do the required calculations and displays. Depending on the number of points and the computer and program design, this might be from two to four seconds. If necessary, the time interval for a specified point can be increased or decreased by adjusting the mainline program to scan the point more or less often. Time intervals of less than one second should not be used.

Coding

Coding is writing a detailed, step-by-step program in the language acceptable to the computer. The programming manual furnished with the computer must be used. A brief example of a program written in BASIC is shown in FIG. 5-30. This covers the start/stop of the supply fan of an air handling unit.

```
14000 REM AH1
14005 GTIME(H,M,S):TMIN=H*60+M
14010 IF TMIN>=ONTIM AND TMIN<=OFFTIM THEN GOTO 14050
14020 REM TIME STP
14025 IF AH01SASF=0 THEN GOTO 15000
14028 REM FAN/OADM OFF, CLOSE HMVV
14030 DOT(1,3)=0:DOT(1,4)=0:AOT(3)=0
14040 MSG$="STATUS:AH01 COMMANDED TO STOP":GOSUB 20050
14045 GOTO 15000
14050 REM TIME STR
14055 IF AH01SASF=1 THEN GOTO 14100
14060 REM OPEN OADM, STRT AH01
14065 DOT(1,4)=1:DOT(1,3)=1
14070 MSG$="STATUS:AH01 COMMANDED TO START":GOSUB 20050
```

Fig. 5-30. Start/stop program.

All program statements are numbered and appear in numerical order. *REM* means remark and is an explanation. The computer does not execute REM statements. More than one statement can appear on each line through the use of a colon (:) to separate the statements.

DOT(1,3) and similar statements refer to a digital output, in this case Channel 3 on Port (Board) 1. *AOT(3)* refers to an analog output on Channel 3 (in some systems this might be the port or board number). *AODM* is the outside air damper. *HMVV* is the humidifier valve.

The program for an analog control output, using PI control, is shown in FIG. 5-31. The value of the zone temperature is read during the general point scan (line 1226). In this example, the system reads the signal as a percent of sensor range. This sensor has a range of 35 degrees F, from 50 to 85 degrees F. Thus, one percent equals 0.35 degrees F, with a zero or start point of 50 degrees F.

The first statement on line 14390 says that the error signal is equal to the measured value of the zone temperature minus a 70 degrees F setpoint (direct-acting, requires a normally closed cooling coil valve). The second statement accumulates the integral *edt* by Simpson's rule. The third statement sets *LSTIM* (last time) equal to the present time, in order to measure the time interval between this scan and the next, for further investigation.

The first statement on line 14410 is the algorithm for PI control (see equation 5-1). A 4 to 20 milliampere output (16 milliampere range) is to be used, so that constant A is at midspan, or 12 milliamperes. The proportional gain is based on the throttling range of 8 degrees F; thus $^{16}/_8 = 2$. The integral

```
1226 AH01TSZN=(.35*AIN(0))+50
......
......
14390 E=AH01TSZN-70:I(2)=I(2)+(E*(TIMER-LSTIM(2))):LSTIM(2)=TIMER
14410 LET OUT=12+2*E+0.00025*I(2):AOT(0)=SPAN(LIM(OUT))
14414 IF AH01TSZN>68 AND AH01TSZN<72 GOTO 14420
14415 MSG$="ALARM:AH1 SPACE TEMPERATURE=":V=AH01TSZN
14416 GOSUB 20000
```

Fig. 5-31. Temperature control program.

gain of 0.00025 is empirical. This gain might, and probably will, be adjusted during the tuning process.

The second statement on line 14410 says that the output signal $AOT(0)$ is equal to "OUT" unless the value exceeds the limits of 4 to 20 milliamperes. The succeeding statements provide for an alarm if the zone temperature is outside of defined limits, or for going on to the next item in the program if zone temperature is within limits.

These are only small examples of the programming required. The language, as already noted, must be that of the computer used.

Getting the software on line and operating as designed involves at least five steps:

1. Testing.
2. Installation.
3. Calibration.
4. Tuning.
5. Troubleshooting.

Testing and installation

Testing is done in two stages. Preliminary testing is done by manually inputting sensor data and observing the reaction of the system. If the preliminary tests indicate that the software is functioning as planned, the software can be installed in the computer. If the programs were written off line, on a computer other than the DDC, they can be installed in the DDC by means of tape or disk, or even downloading from the master computer. If the programs were compiled directly on the DDC, no further installation is necessary. Final testing occurs under actual operating conditions after calibrating and tuning have been done and the system being controlled is known to be operating satisfactorily.

Calibration

Calibration is required for each and every sensor, whether analog or digital, to make sure that the computer is receiving accurate data. Each sensor point must be tested to make sure that the signal being received represents the true state of the variable being sensed. For example, the actual value of the temperature must be checked with a laboratory thermometer and compared to the signal received at the DDC. The appropriate value is calculated from the signal, using the sensor characteristics furnished by the manufacturer. The computer software, if properly written, will interpret the signal as the correct value of the variable, for display and for use in the control algorithm. A digital signal is simpler but must indicate an open or closed contact in the mode appropriate to the state of the variable.

Output signals also must be calibrated to make sure they provide the correct information to the controlled devices. Setpoint reset values should be observed and analyzed for conformance to reset schedules. Two-position outputs must be appropriate to the control sequence desired.

This procedure is fairly straightforward and not too difficult, but it does take time and care. Without careful calibration, to assure the operator that the data are credible, further effort will not yield satisfactory results.

Tuning

The tuning of an analog control loop is, theoretically, a simple process. For the best performance — minimum offset with stable operation — the usual procedure is to increase the gain until the system becomes unstable then decrease the gain somewhat below the point where stability is obtained. With a simple pneumatic or electronic controller, gain is adjusted with a screwdriver. With DDC, gain is adjusted by changing numbers in software. In either case, the initial value of the gain is usually empirical, because so little is known about the time constants in an HVAC system. The final value is affected by the operating characteristics of the HVAC system — the so-called system gains.

With a DDC system, the usual control mode is PI, as described above. For a DDC system with a discrete time interval between any two readings of the variable (sampling rate or sampling time), the time interval also has an effect on the gain. Increasing the sampling rate increases the gain.

The usual procedure for tuning a DDC control loop is to set the proportional gain for a wide throttling range (for example, 10 degrees F for temperature). The integral gain and sampling rate can then be adjusted to provide maximum performance with stability.

Final testing and troubleshooting

In the ideal situation, tuning the loop really is simple. In the real world, nonideal situation, the tuning process is complicated by the real life response of the HVAC system. (See reference 2 at the end of this section.) With the information the DDC provides about the HVAC system operation, it is possible to analyze problems more readily than with conventional controls. Most of the time it is possible to determine the source of the problem — the controls or the HVAC system or, more often, a little of both.

Correcting a control problem involves:

1. Replacing or recalibrating a control device.
2. Replacing a defective board in the DDC.
3. Modifying the software.

Correcting the HVAC system problem requires a good understanding of HVAC systems, using the information obtained by the DDC to the greatest extent possible. A typical problem in a VAV system is the change in system gain as the air flow rate changes. The cooling coil and its control valve might be properly sized for a linear response at design air flow rate. However, at 50 percent of design flow, the coil and valve become considerably oversized. The control loop must be tuned to avoid instability at low flow rates, which means there will be less than ideal response at high flow rates. Many other system problems will be found. The DDC allows you to analyze and isolate the problems, but it does not substitute for experience, common sense, and an understanding of basic principles.

Summary

This briefly discusses the process of providing software for a DDC system. It requires proper system preparation, an understanding of control theory and computer language, and experience with HVAC systems and control principles. Most people would like to know more about all these areas. The design professional who does not acquire this kind of education soon will be in trouble. Technology does not change basic principles, but it does change the way you apply them.

References

1. "Proportional-plus-Integral Control" in part 2 of this book.
2. "System Gains" in part 2 of this book.

*   *   *

Some of the technology described here is somewhat outdated, partially because manufacturers are trying to make field software simpler by providing pretested software packages for practically any function. Even so, it is still necessary to go through all of the operations described here except the actual coding. Neglect any of these steps at your risk. And, if you have the ability, it is still possible to write software from scratch. It just takes time (and money!).

List of Abbreviations

A

ac	alternating current
A/C	air conditioning
A/D	analog/digital convertor
ADP	apparatus dew point
AHU	air-handling unit
AI	analog in
AO	analog out
ASHRAE	American Society of Heating, Refrigeration, and Air Conditioning Engineers, Incorporated

B

Btuh	British thermal units per hour

C

C	common port; terminal; ° centigrade
cfm	cubic feet per minute
CHW	chilled water
CLF	cooling load factor
COP	coefficient of performance
CPA	control point adjustment
CPU	central processing unit
CRT	cathode ray tube
C_v	valve sizing coefficient
CW(S)	condensing water (supply)

D

D/A	digital/analog convertor
db	dry bulb (temperature)
dc	direct current
DD	double duct (AHU)
DDC	direct-digital control (or controller)
deg	degrees (temperature)
delta T, ΔT	temperature difference
DI	digital in
DO	digital out
DP, delta P, ΔP	pressure difference
DX	direct expansion (refrigeration)

E

EBTR	emergency building temperature regulations
EIA	Electronics Industries Association
EMCS	energy management and control system
EP	electric-pneumatic

F

F	° Fahrenheit
FID	field interface device
h	enthalpy

HEPA	high-efficiency absolute filter
HPAC	*Heating/Piping/Air Conditioning* magazine
HV	heating and ventilating
HVAC	heating, ventilating, and air conditioning

I

IFID	intelligent FID
in. wg	inches of water gauge (pressure)
IEEE	Institute of Electrical and Electronics Engineers
I/O	input/output
I/P	current-to-pressure conversion

K

kw(h)	kilowatt (hours)

L

LSI	large-scale integration

M

ma	milliamperes (current)
MAP	manufacturing automation protocol
MCS	monitoring and control system
MUX	multiplexer; multiplexing
MZ	multizone AHU

N

NC	normally closed (port or contact)
NEMA	National Electrical Manufacturers' Association
NO	normally open (port or contact)
NSF	National Science Foundation

P

P	pressure or proportional control mode
PC	personal computer
PCC	process control computer
PE	pneumatic-electric
PI	proportional plus integral control mode
P/I	pressure-to-current conversion
PPU	portable programming unit
PRV	pressure reducing valve
psi	pounds per square inch (pressure)

R

rh	relative humidity
RTD	resistance temperature detector

S

SAT	supply air temperature
SC	shading coefficient
SCR	silicon-controlled rectifier
SHFG	sensible heat gain factor
SP	static pressure
S/T	sensible/total heat ratio

T

T	temperature

V

v	volts
vac	volts ac (alternating current)
VAV	variable air volume
vdc	volts dc (direct current)

W

w	specific humidity
wb	wet bulb (temperature)
wc	water column

Index